Never Sleep
with a
Fat Man
in July

Also by Modine Gunch

Never Heave Your Bosom in a Front-Hook Bra

Never Sleep with a Fat Man in July

Modine Gunch

CREATED BY
LIZ SCOTT

ST. MARTIN'S PRESS / NEW YORK

Thanks, Mike

NEVER SLEEP WITH A FAT MAN IN JULY. Copyright © 1990, 1991, 1992, 1993 by Liz Scott. All rights reserved. Printed in the United States of America. No part of this book may be used or reproduced in any manner whatsoever without written permission except in the case of brief quotations embodied in critical articles or reviews. For information, address St. Martin's Press, 175 Fifth Avenue, New York, N.Y. 10010.

Library of Congress Cataloging-in-Publication Data
Gunch, Modine.
Never sleep with a fat man in July / Modine Gunch (created by Liz Scott)
p. cm.
ISBN 0-312-09883-9
I. Title.
PN6162.G835 1993
814'.54—dc20
93-8997
CIP

First Edition: October 1993

10 9 8 7 6 5 4 3 2 1

Acknowledgments

~~~~~~~~~~

Sherry Heller, Rosemary Ruiz Lewis, Andre the Giant, Robert Scott, the sweaty man at the Louisiana Drivers' License Bureau, Kevin Costner, Mary Jane Brodrick LaCoste, Hobbes the Cat, Mike Scott, Geraldo, Angela Hill, the Pulitzer Prize Committee, Tom Cruise, Betsy Scott, Robin Rue, Bridget Scott, Scott Bakula, Sister Helen Prejean, C.S.J., Jabba the Hutt, John Clark, Fine Art, Katy Scott, Arlette Bouvier, Daniel Day-Lewis, Flo Scott, Everybody at *New Orleans* magazine, Everybody at the Weather Bureau, Miss Probst, St. Jude, Jed Mattes, Michael Denneny, Anne Rice, Oprah, the inventor of the egg prescrambler, Kelly Scott, Keith Kahla, Elena Marina, Lesley Scott, Bill Abbott, John Clark, Vincent Heller, Elvis.

Contents

~~~~~~

Introduction

~~~~~~~~~

The stories in this book are more or less true, although I have been warned not to admit that.

Modine Gunch is, heavily diguised, me. And you. And every woman who puts up with the hassles of jobs, kids, cars, cat hairs, high heels, and the world at large.

She's wiry and energetic and upbeat and undefeated—a soul sister who talks like she's from New Jersey. (This is because she's from New Orleans. Everybody talks like that around here.)

But we all know where she's really coming from. Home.

—Liz Scott

Never Sleep with a Fat Man in July

~~~~~~~~~~

Never sleep with a fat man in July. That's the advice my Mama should have give me.

Now don't get the wrong idea. I am just talking about SLEEPING. None of that other stuff. This ain't no Dr. Ruth book.

I don't know if it is true for skinny men, but fat men are like space heaters that snore. When my husband Lout flops in bed, the temperature of that bed shoots up a easy ten degrees, and it got nothing to do with passion.

Now in the winter this ain't so bad. I can warm up my feet by holding them close to Lout's back like he was a fireplace. I got to be careful, though, because if I actually touch him, he shrieks and carries on like my mother-in-law did that time she dropped the frozen yogurt cone down her front at Audubon Zoo. But that's another story. Lout better just get used to my feet. He married all of me, so tough.

In July, of course, I don't need him to warm up my

feet. But it's hard to keep them or any other part of me away from him, because naturally the bed sinks way down low on his side and I got to fight the law of gravity. I sleep every night with one arm and one leg flung over the side of the bed just so I stay in place.

Not to mention, the side which Lout sleeps on got all the advantages. He is next to the window with the air conditioner and he soaks up all the cold air. Either his body sucks it in like a sponge, or he just inhales it all. Anyway, not much gets to me. And right next to the air conditioner is the bedside TV, which I can't watch unless I sit up in bed because I sure can't see over Lout laying down.

But, worst of all, he's got the bathroom on his side. And I am one of those people who have to get up in the middle of the night to go. Generally I get up in a hurry, so I just leapfrog over him instead of walking around. Nothing wrong with this—it probably gives me exercise. But when I had to help chaperon my daughter Gumdrop's Girl Scout camp-out in Covington, we all slept in these little cabins with bunk beds, and I got a top bunk. So when I woke up at night, before I remembered where I was, I leapfrogged over the side of the bed and landed on top of the assistant troop leader in the next upper bunk. I don't know what that woman thinks of me to this day.

Why don't I just get Lout to switch sides? Because then I'd be on the low side is why, and he would roll downhill and I would be squashed like a roach. I guess

I could turn the mattress if my son Gargoyle hadn't been parking his bubble gum underneath it all these years.

Anyway, all of this I can put up with. There is only one thing I can't put up with. Lout loves his sleep, and he sleeps deep. He climbs in bed, and he turns around three times like a dog, and he settles down, and sighs, and scratches, and then he gets quiet. And just when I am about to drop off, he gives out with this sound like he was vacuuming out a tuba. I sit up straight in bed and clutch my bosom, but now Lout gets very, very quiet. About the time I decide he is dead, he roars into a encore, only louder. It's like them foghorns on the river would sound if they was mating in your backyard. This is not a noise you can block with a pillow over your head and your fingers in your ears. You can't do nothing but drag off the sheet and go sleep on the couch. But if I do that, Lout will think I don't love him no more.

The doctor says Lout wouldn't snore so much if he was in better shape, but Lout got no plans to change his shape. I myself noticed that he mostly snores in summer when the air conditioner is on, and I guess I could always turn it off and let us both sweat to death, and pray he goes first. But there has got to be a nicer way.

I know I need to do something, because by morning Lout is all rested and looking at me lovey-dovey, and I ain't looking back.

Finally I go weeping and wailing to my sister-in-law, Larva. "I am going to tell you a family secret, Modine,"

Larva says to me. "You want to know why they got so many Gunches in New Orleans? It's because Gunch marriages wear like iron. We all keep a Bible on the bedstand."

Now I am as religious as the next person, but I am wondering how this is going to help. She keeps on talking. "When the snoring starts up, you just reach over and knock that Bible on the floor—SLAM!—and Lout will sit up straight in bed. He won't know what woke him up. When he looks at you, you pretend you are sleeping like a angel. And you just fall asleep, real quick, while he is wandering around checking the doors and windows."

And would you believe, it works like a charm. So this how you sleep with a fat man in July. If your Mama don't tell you, I did.

Who's the Boss? The Kid Who's Carsick

~~~~~~~~

S ome people say the oldest kid in the family gets the most attention. Some say no, it is the oldest boy. Some claim it is the baby. All of them are wrong. The kid who really gets treated special is the one who gets carsick. You put three kids in a car, and if that kid says he wants a window, he's got it. He says he wants to stop, you stop right NOW. No way are you going to argue with somebody who is turning green and gurgling right in front of your eyes.

In our family, the carsick one is my son Gargoyle. Now my mother-in-law, Miss Larda, tells me to just put Gargoyle in the front seat because it is less bumpy in front, and he will not get sick. So I do, and I sit in the back right behind him, but he does get sick and I find out that anything that goes out the window in front is going to go right in the window in back. This is how I lose faith in my mother-in-law.

Besides, we are finding out other terrible truths

about driving with kids. There is a direct relationship between the amount of time it takes you to get somewhere and the number of kids you got in the backseat. With three of them, you got to make three times as many rest stops as before, because naturally none of them want to rest at the same time. I don't think they should call them rest stops anyway. We sure don't go there to rest. We go there to use the rest rooms, which I know for sure nobody ever rests in. They ought to call them relief rooms.

There is one just the other side of the Mississippi state line that we never stop at no matter how much we need relief. We went there one time just after little Gladiola was potty trained. I stayed out in the car, and my older daughter Gumdrop went in with her. And she don't realize that Gladiola is crawling from stall to stall, locking each one from the inside, until she crawls out the last one. Gumdrop don't know what to do about this, so she don't do nothing. They stroll back to the car and they don't tell us for another hundred miles what went on.

And I look back along that highway and I know why there is hardly any traffic behind us. I can imagine all them ladies lined up at the stalls waiting. Once they figured out what happened, they probably would've formed a mob and come after us if they didn't all have to find a place to use the bathroom first.

Finally Miss Larda decides to solve the vacation problem by renting this cottage by the lake, about a hour away. It even has a name: "The Pot of Gold at Rainbow's End." She tells us all to come over there— Lout's brothers, Leech and Lurch, and his sister Larva and her kids. Leech and Lurch are happy because they figure they won't have nothing to do but drink beer and lay on the fishing pier and belch. Larva and myself are glad because we can finally teach the youngest kids to swim. Larva's little boy, Locust, is so terrified of water I actually seen him walk around a mud puddle once, and you know that ain't normal.

So Miss Larda goes up there and she leaves us this map with directions. Next day, the rest of us go. Lout and myself lead, and Larva and her kids follow behind in their car, and Leech and Lurch follow them. And off we go, three in a row. I got the map and I am calling out directions to Lout. After a while, I tell him it is going to be just around this bend coming up and to hang a hard right. But Lout hangs a LEFT, so Larva hangs one and Leech and Lurch hang one and there we go, three in a row, heading into a automatic car wash.

Lout, naturally, don't never make mistakes, so he just drives right in. I say "This ain't 'The Pot of Gold,' " and he says, "Need to get these bugs off the wind- shield," like I am going to believe that. I roll up the windows, and I glance back through the jet spray to see Larva right behind us, looking like she is in shock, and her windows are wide open. Then I hear a screech like a fire siren and I know Locust is wet.

As soon as we get through, I jump out and go find

the manager. I say, "Can you help me? I am looking for The Pot . . ." but he cuts me off and says, "Right around back, ma'am," and hands me a key with a slab of wood attached. So I decide to just take a side trip in there and let Lout settle this. I do and I shut the door behind me, and it clicks, and I realize I can't open it again.

Outside, I can hear Locust still yowling, and Gargoyle trying to get his share of attention by yelling he is going to throw up NOW, and Lurch and Leech telling the manager they shouldn't have to pay for a car wash they got by accident, and Larva saying she wants to see that stupid map. Nobody can hear me thunking my body against the rest-room door. I think I'm going to wind up resting in there after all. Maybe all night.

Finally it gets quiet. The manager hears me, I guess, because he comes over and pulls open the door and I sort of fall out. Gargoyle and Locust are both sucking on peppermint sticks, which come free with the car washes that Lout has finally offered to pay for. Larva has the map, and she says she will lead the way from now on. So we all jump in our cars and screech around back and forth making U-turns, and then we line up behind Larva and drive off, three in a row, to Miss Larda's camp.

Nothing like relaxing.

Hair Today, Gone Tomorrow

~~~~~~~~~~

I tell you, sometimes I just wish I was bald. Life would be a lot easier.

Hair is just not worth the trouble and grief. Now, I am not talking about armpit hair and like that, which of course you can just shave off. I am talking about a woman's crown and glory.

In New Orleans, either it is damp out or it is raining. If your hair is naturally straight, you can set it in little tiny curlers and try to sleep on them all night, and you can get up in the morning and brush it out and touch it up with the hot rollers and look at yourself in the mirror and you are gorgeous. Then you step outside. And on your way to the bus stop you can feel them curls starting to droop, and your bangs, which were in these cute little waves over your forehead, have slid down over your eyes. You need to know how bad it is, so you naturally kind of scootch down to catch your reflection in the windows of cars parked along the curb. Then somebody inside of one of them screams. God knows what they were doing in there at eight o'clock in the morning that they think you saw.

Anyway, by the time you get to work, you got the coiffure of a string mop.

My sister-in-law Larva got naturally curly hair, and the same thing happens to her in reverse. She says she sets her hair on real big rollers to make it fall in soft flattering waves like the commercials say, but the minute she walks out into the wet, them waves take on a life of their own and shrivel up into a million matted-up balls. "Don't talk to me about crowns and glory, Modine," she says to me. "That don't mean much to a woman who is going through life looking like she is growing Spanish moss on her head."

My girlfriend Awlette does my hair. She works at this hair salon near my house. I got to be careful with Awlette, though, because while she got a good heart, she got sort of gaudy taste.

Anyway, one time I got talked into chaperoning my daughter Gumdrop's spring formal at Celibacy Academy, and I decide to do it up right and get myself fixed up. So I make a appointment with Awlette. Right away, while Awlette is washing my head, she starts asking questions that let me know I'm in for trouble. First she says, "How about a fun little hairdo, Modine? One you can play with?"

Why do these hairdressers always think you want to do that? Standing in front of the bathroom mirror with my elbows up over my head fooling with my hair is not my idea of play. If I want fun, I'll go lay on the couch and watch "Jeopardy."

So I tell Awlette just to stick to my regular style. She says okay but do I want a little something to cover that white. I figure she just got a extra batch of coloring she wants to use up, because I don't have white hair, even though with them kids of mine I have earned some. I tell her just to forget it. So she gives me my regular cut and perm and I go home.

I walk in the door and my husband Lout looks at me and he says, "Did you have to pay extra for the streaks?" I look in the mirror and what do I see but white streaks—streaks that didn't even show until I decided to improve myself and get fixed up.

I race over to the drugstore for hair coloring, and I go in the bathroom and lather it in. But the chemical that was in the perm must have combined with the chemical that was in the dye or something, because when I am finished all my hair is green.

I cry awhile. Then I tell Lout not to speak to me. Then I wrap a towel around my head and go back to the drugstore, looking like a Arab with allergies, and search through the shelves and I can't find a thing that says it will take out the green. Finally I call Awlette.

She don't cackle in my ear or nothing. She is very calm. She says this happens a lot to women who try to color their hair theirselves, and that believe it or not, I can fix it by rubbing cigarette ashes in my hair.

I think about that one awhile. Nobody in our house smokes, but Lout's brothers Leech and Lurch live next door and they do. I tell Lout to call them up and tell them we need their ashes right NOW.

Of course, they don't get it straight. They come rushing into my kitchen, not bringing anything, and tell me Lout said to get their butts right over. I say, not BUTTS, ASHES. And they tell me their asses ARE over here, and what does Lout want? I finally explain, very slow.

Anyway, the ashes work, I guess, because I go to Gumdrop's formal and nobody laughs in my face.

But I still wish I was bald.

Falling into Fashion
(or Her Cups Are
Filled to Overflowing)

~~~~~~~

E very year it is the same thing. It is August. You walk into a department store to get out of the heat and you look around and it is like Willard Scott has predicted the ice age was coming. You are standing there in your shorts and flip-flop sandals and you are looking at seventeen racks of hooded coats.

Why do the stores do that? Now I know somewhere on this planet leaves are falling and breezes are blowing. But I got news for them, honey. There ain't no falling and blowing going on around here. This is New Orleans. It is hot. You want to make a fashion statement? Go waltzing out the door in them fall clothes and you got your fashion statement. You are stating that you are out of your mind.

I tell that to my sister-in-law Gloriosa, but does she listen? No, she just stands there with sweat running down the back of her argyle sweater and tells me I am not supposed to wear white after Labor Day.

Who made up that rule, I want to know? Some dress manufacturers from up North? What do they know? They act like they are making clothes for a bunch of Barbie dolls. Look at what they give us. Bras with adjustable straps that come apart when you adjust them so you got to tie a knot in them before you run out the house. Bras with no straps at all. Dresses with zippers that you got to yank up underneath your arm.

And, of course, the all-time winner. High heels. High heels are like roaches. They were here before we were born and they will probably be here long after we are all dead. You know why? They hurt, that's why. That is the secret of their survival. You prance out with your sexy high heels on, and what do you do as soon as you get where you are going? Kick them off. Them shoes spend all their time stuck under desks and chairs and church pews while you go around in your stocking feet. No wonder they live longer than you. Besides, they are hazardous to your health. You get up in the morning, running late for work, and you rush around trying to put everything on at once, and you jump into your high heels and then you lean over to brush your hair upside-down to give it body and what happens? You fall on your head, that's what happens. Who needs that grief?

I got a few more fashion statements to make. After thousands of years of civilization, they have finally got to the point where they can make clothes that you don't have to iron, and what do they do? They go back to making cotton clothes. And then they BRAG about them. They sew in these cutesy little labels that read "I am 100 percent cotton." This means "Somebody is going to have to iron a million wrinkles out of me every time they wear me, and I am going to be a mess again in five minutes." I can tell you this: If permanent press was a religion, I would be a nun.

Of course, this ain't nothing compared to the silk clothes you can't get wet. This means you can't get caught in the rain in them. You can't walk past a lawn sprinkler in them. And you sure can't hold no babies. Know what I think? I think some clothes need labels that says "Not fit for human wearing."

My husband Lout says neckties should have warning labels like that. He read in the papers that a man can pass out from wearing a necktie. For instance, when he twists his head around to back out his own driveway, his tie can press down on one of his major veins and he'll plop right over. So Lout decides he is not going to dress up and drive. It is as bad as drinking and driving, he says. This ain't exactly going to be a big change in his lifestyle, so I don't say nothing.

Of course, he wasn't always like that. When we first started going out, Lout used to get all dressed up. And so did I. And I had problems worse than neckties. One time I wear this cute little strapless dress with, of course, my strapless padded bra underneath. I hook it up so tight I can't take a deep breath, to keep it from slithering down. But in the car on the way to the restaurant, I feel it slither down anyway.

We pull into the parking lot and I know I better not wait for Lout to act like a gentleman and come around and open the door for me. Because this outfit is not going to stand up when I stand up. So I jump out quick and hook my thumbs into the top of the dress and haul up. The dress comes up all right, but the bra is still down. I remember the lady in the lingerie department said the proper way to put on a bra is to bend from the waist and fall into your cups. I bend over and wiggle around and hope to God I am falling in my cups. Just then Lout comes around the car and stops short. I know his jaw has dropped down to the ground. I stand up to explain, but now I got two rows of breasts. If that ain't a fashion statement, I don't know what is.

And would your believe, while I am in the little girls' room adjusting myself, Lout makes up his mind to marry me. I guess he figured he knew everything now.

Waiting for Godzilla

~~~~~~~~~~

I am reading the list of what the weather bureau is going to name hurricanes this year, and at least I got one thing to be grateful for. They didn't name none after me. That's what they did last year.

Not Hurricane Modine. That would have been bad enough. It is worse. It's Hurricane Nana. Can you believe? Nana. Now there's a real vicious name for you.

It's my name, too, because it is short for Nanan, which is what most people around here call their godmothers. I am godmother to my precious little niece Pupa, my sister-in-law Larva's baby. This means I am the one that is going to come up with the best presents every year for Pupa's birthday and her dance review and all the other stuff. When she thinks "Nana," she is supposed to think sweetness and light and lots of loot, not torrents and rain and howling winds. I just thank God this Hurricane Nana didn't actually come and blow away half the city. That would sure have besmirched my image.

Who are the people in charge of naming these hurricanes anyway? I would hate to meet their Nanas. They were probably the type who gave them stuff like socks and spiritual bouquets for their birthdays, and messed up their entire childhoods.

Something must have made them strange. Look at the names they pick this year for future killer hurricanes. Danny. Larry. Mindy. Sure don't make no chills run up and down my spine. No wonder they got trouble getting people to evacuate. Is anybody going to flee from the fury of Mindy? No, they are just going to stand around and look smug and wait for some television reporter to stick a microphone in front of their face and ask them why they are not evacuating. Then they can fold their arms and say, "Well, Geraldo, we've weathered a whole lot of hurricanes right here. So I guess we'll just sit and wait for Mindy. Drink a few beers to pass the time. Heh, heh."

But if these hurricanes had the right kind of names, them people would get theirselves moving. Something like Godzilla. King Kong. Jaws. Can you see somebody standing around with their arms folded saying they are just going to sit and have a few beers while they wait for Hurricane Godzilla? They would be long gone before any TV reporters got there, if the TV reporters even had the nerve to show up.

Them weather people need to start using a little imagination.

I was thinking about this when I snuck out the

house for a hamburger one day, and they were giving out hurricane tracking charts with the food. On the back they have a bunch of hurricane safety rules.

The first one says you should fill up the bathtub. I think about that awhile. The entire lake is going to be dumped into the city, but we will all drown with our bathtubs full. I do it anyway. I was brought up Catholic, so I never argue much.

Then they tell you to stock up on the emergency necessities, which is, of course, bread, batteries and beer, masking tape, and a St. Jude candle. I know that routine. I always tell the kids to tape up the windows while I go see if everything outside is secure—the garbage cans, the old radiator from my husband Lout's truck, and the plastic Santa Claus and sleigh that he hides in the hedge instead of putting up in the attic after Christmas. They all look secure to me, so we leave.

Our family and Lout's brothers Leech and Lurch, and Larva and her kids and his other sister Gloriosa always go to my mother-in-law's for Christmas and Easter and hurricanes because she got two refrigerators and those are the times we all like to eat a lot. Her house is also the best for hurricanes because it is two stories high, so if one of them flash floods gets in we can all run upstairs, and if the roof blows off we can all run downstairs. If both things happen: the roof goes and the house floods, we are going to get wet no matter where we are, so I bring raincoats and umbrellas for upstairs and rubber rafts for downstairs.

Lout's mama, Miss Larda, always gives Lout a hatchet and tells him to put it up in the attic. That way if the water rises real high we can float up there on our rubber rafts and if the roof is still there we can chop our way out. Now we are ready for anything.

Miss Larda fries a few chickens and I bring three or four pecan pies, and Leech and Lurch have some six-packs and a couple boxes of doughnuts and Larva comes over with her kids and stuffed eggplants. And we all sit down to wait it out. And we all put on about twenty pounds waiting, which is probably our best defense. Even Godzilla ain't going to blow us away.

How the Gunch
Stole Halloween

~~~~~~~~~~

O ne thing my kids got to admit—they always got real scary costumes for Halloween. This is because scary is ugly, and ugly is a lot easier to make than pretty. You don't got to sit down and sew no green velvet dinosaur outfits or satin pumpkin suits. Who is that going to scare? What you do is something simple, like dye the kid green and let some ketchup ooze down his forehead. Then he can go scare the velvet pants off them dinosaurs. Now, if you got a older kid, like my son Gargoyle, who decides he wants to be sophisticated, you got complications. My sister-in-law Gloriosa says I should just sling the toilet seat around his neck, hand him a water pistol, and tell him he's a bidet. But then, Gloriosa got no taste at all.

My kids love Halloween, but not as much as my husband Lout's brothers, Leech and Lurch. They say ; is the one day of the year they can get back at the pesky kids. They used to just do mild things, like wh the kids would come up the walk, look at him nervous, with their Mama behind them, and sing "Trick or treat," Leech would start opening up the door real slow, saying "Ye-e-es?" in a creaky old lady voice, to get their nerves on edge. Then Lurch would slip out the bushes a couple inches behind them and BLAST this air horn he had. That would send all the kids flying. And the Mamas too. Leech and Lurch said they were sorry about the Mamas, but a good scare is just what kids need, get those little adrenaline pumps started up early in life. And they never had to give out no candy.

Every year, they dream up something new and terrible: dropping out of trees in a gorilla costume, or hiding under the steps with their hands in cold water and reaching up and grabbing somebody's leg. Stuff like that. But a couple years ago, right after Leech got that job at Charity Hospital, them two lunatics thought of a stunt they figured would top everything.

First I got to explain something. Leech and Lurch live with my mother-in-law, Miss Larda, and most times of the year she keeps a pretty close eye on them. But at Halloween she is distracted, because the next day is All Saints' Day. In New Orleans, All Saints' Day is the day to go to the cemetery and check on your expired friends and relatives; maybe tidy up their graves and put out fresh chrysanthemums and say a few Hail Marys and then go get some fried chicken and go home. Well, Miss Larda, she knows a whole lot of dead people, so All Saints' Day is very busy for her.

This year she makes Leech use his day off to dr[...]
her down to the cemeteries a week before All Sain[...]
Day, so she can check around and see if she has to [...]
new liners for the vases or anything. While she is nosi[...]
around, Leech goes off with a cloth sack and com[...]
back with something in it, she don't think to ask wha[...]
and he heaves it in the back, and they go off home. A[...]
she don't give that sack another thought until the mor[...]
ing of Halloween, when she walks into her bathroo[...]
and there is a skeleton lying in the tub.

Well, she shrieks and runs around the hous[...]
awhile, but Leech is at work and Lurch is God know[...]
where. So finally she goes and looks at this skeleto[...]
some more. It isn't hitched together or anything, it i[...]
just bones lying there. And she thinks about Leech an[...]
that bag, and how here he is desecrating a grave just t[...]
scare some kids on Halloween, and this is probabl[...]
somebody's grandmother laying here in her bathtub[...]
Well, you got to give Miss Larda credit. She is made o[...]
strong stuff. She knows what she got to do. She gets two
shopping bags, and she puts half the skeleton in one and
half in the other, and she goes outside and catches the
bus to the cemeteries.

What she don't know is that this ain't no grandmother. These bones are plastic. Lurch swiped the skeleton all right, but he just swiped it out a box from the
educational equipment room at the hospital. He laid out
the bones in the bathtub so he could wire them together
to look realistic. What he had in the bag was rocks to lay

out like a grave on the lawn for Halloween, and he was going to fix this skeleton to rise up out of it.

But she don't know that, and she gets off the bus at the cemeteries, and she tiptoes up and down the rows of tombs looking for one that has been broken into. The old cemeteries in New Orleans got all the tombs built above the ground, thank God, so she don't have to carry a shovel. Finally she finds one with a wide crack, so she makes sure nobody is looking, and then she takes out those bones one at a time, and she drops them in the crack like she was dropping them in a mail slot. PLUNK, PLUNK, PLUNK. Then she takes a little bottle of holy water out her purse and splashes it on the crack, and she folds up her shopping bags and she catches her bus home.

And that's how the plastic skeleton got blessed and interred in somebody's tomb. And that's how Leech lost his job. He and Lurch were so upset, they went out to the Sloth Lounge and didn't scare any little kids that year, so Miss Larda had to give out all the candy in the house and dip into her Mardi Gras beads before they finally stopped coming. And their Mamas never found out what a narrow escape they had.

The Red Bird of
Happiness

~~~~~~~~

Every Thanksgiving morning it is the same thing. I am tearing apart the kitchen, looking for the bag of giblets which I probably never took out the turkey before I put it in the oven. Or I have found cat footprints on top the candied yams. Something like that. I am not thankful. I am hysterical.

Meanwhile my husband Lout is flopped in front the TV wanting to know if somebody will please get him a beer.

On other holidays, the whole family goes to eat at my mother-in-law Larda Gunch's house, but on this one she is gearing up to hit the stores for them day-after-Thanksgiving sales and she is too busy planning her strategy to fool with no turkey.

So all the Gunches come to our house, instead. This is bad enough. But last Thanksgiving starts off even worse than usual. My sister-in-law Gloriosa usually brings whole wheat garlic bread or festive tofu with sage or whatever she is into at the time. This year, what she is into is her new boyfriend, Rocco. So she is bringing him.

As soon as Leech and Lurch hear that Gloriosa is bringing a date, they get it into their heads to bring these girls, Chicklette and Trinkette. AND, they inform me, they don't want to eat at the card table no more.

Well. Most years I sit the adults at the main table, the kids in the kitchen, and Leech and Lurch at the card table over the floor furnace, which they never complained about before, because it keeps their feet warm and also their dinner. But no-o, not this year, they say. They are both over thirty now, so they want to be treated like grown men.

When Miss Larda hears about this one, she goes through the roof. She don't care where they sit, but she don't approve of Trinkette and Chicklette. She says her boys hang around with them for "one purpose only." She don't say what the purpose is, but I think it is free beer, because their brother is a bartender. I personally don't think Leech and Lurch care about any other purposes. Anyway, if they are going to sit at the main table, Miss Larda says she herself will sit at the card table.

But come Thanksgiving morning, I got a disaster that makes me forget about card tables and everything else. I go to preheat the oven, and it don't preheat. It is stone cold dead. Miss Larda has been telling me for years I should clean that oven. But I never seen no point in it. Who is going to look around inside a oven? Anybody who puts their head in a oven is not in a mood to be worrying about housekeeping.

But now I think maybe she was right.

I know I got to do something fast. I think about barbecuing the turkey, but I can imagine the number of charcoal briquettes we are going to have to use up to do that. Then I look over next to the barbecue pit, at the crawfish cooker. Ours is a big one that comes up to my waist, and it got its own gas burner. I remember seeing on this TV cooking show how somebody deep-fried a turkey in one of them things. Now, I can't afford enough oil to fill up a crawfish cooker. But I can afford enough water to fill it up. I decide to boil this turkey.

So I do. And a few hours later, when the Gunches and the stuffing are all ready, my husband Lout and me, we go haul the turkey into the kitchen and plop it on a platter. Well, I can see right then that it don't look like no gourmet delight. Instead of being nice and plump and brown looking, it is dead white and slimy. This is going to be a great Thanksgiving, I am thinking, with everybody mad and now a turkey that looks like it fell in the canal and drowned.

And then I get struck by inspiration. Red gravy. The Gunches got enough Italian in them to love that, and it is sure a festive color. So I open up five cans of tomato sauce and I heat it up to thicken it, and I slather it all over this bird. And now I got a turkey that looks like something.

What it looks like is the world's biggest meatball.

The gravy kind of covers up the turkey shape so what is on the platter looks round. Big and round and red. And when I carry it in, the Gunches gasp all right, but it ain't the same kind of gasp they usually give when they see food. It is the kind of gasp you give when you see a really obese lady on a nudie calendar.

I ignore that. Lout cuts it up and I serve it around, and act like nothing is different. Then I notice everybody has stopped glaring at each other and they are staring at this red turkey like they are hypnotized. I guess they don't know what to make of it because they all eat very quietly and nobody says nothing mean in front of me. Afterwards, they take the toothpicks over to the TV, like usual, and pass them around. Miss Larda is so distracted, she sits on the couch right between Chicklette and Trinkette.

So the tomato turkey turns out to be a dove of peace. And even though I am stuck in the kitchen with the carcass, again, I finally feel thankful.

Automatic Cat Wash

~~~~~~~

D id you ever fall for that trick back in high school where the teacher passes out this real long, hard test and at the top it says, "This is not really a test. Just sit at your desk and twiddle your thumbs." Naturally nobody reads the directions and everybody starts writing like crazy. The teacher—it was Sister Gargantua who did it to me—sits back in her long black habit, cackling at you behind her hand. The object of her little joke is to teach you to always read the directions.

Well, I was thinking about writing Sister and telling her she taught us wrong. We are better off never reading most directions. Take "Cook for five minutes or until done." Notice they give you a choice. Five minutes if you want to eat it raw; or until it's really cooked, but they ain't going to tell you when that might be. Or "Wash with like colors only" on a shirt that is purple, green, and gold. Or "Iron with warm iron if desired."

Who desires to iron, I ask you that. What they mean is "Iron with warm iron if don't desire to look like slept under the house." And on rearview mirrors "Objects in mirror may be closer than they appear" What "objects"? How much closer? You going to have to turn around and look to find that out. And if you got to turn around, what you got a rearview mirror for?

Sometimes it is the stuff they don't say. Like on them bubble packages they must make out of cast-iron clear plastic. They should say, "Do not waste time slashing at this with car key. You are going to have to go home and get out the butcher knife."

And hair dryers. To read their directions, you'd think all you could dry was your hair. They don't say you can dry the insides of tennis shoes, if you can stand the smell. Or when you yank your clean pantyhose off the shower rod and pull them on and then you realize the cotton crotch is still damp, you can grab that hair dryer and take care of that without even taking them off, as long as one of the kids don't see you.

Last Christmas Lout's sister Gloriosa gave us one of them popcorn poppers that you're supposed to use over a fireplace. It is like two little bowls made out of screen that clamp together and it got a long handle so you can stick it directly into the flames. That's what the directions say. Only problem is we ain't got no fireplace. Now I know I could figure out a way to use it on the floor furnace, but why bother when we got a electric popper?

So I shove it down under the sink and if it rusts before I think up a use for it, I will throw it out.

In March I am up on the roof, pulling oak leaves out of the gutters (which my husband Lout should be doing but he got a important ball game to watch). And I come across this little bird nest, and there are these three baby birds in it, stark naked. I know this nest is going to be washed away with the first rain, unless I scoop it up some way and put it in a tree. And all of a sudden I think of a use for that long-handled popper. I yell down to my daughter Gumdrop to go get the popcorn popper so I can save these birds. Naturally, she starts to argue, but I tell her to HURRY UP because I can't crouch up here on the roof all day. She disappears and she is gone a long, long time, and finally I hear her coming up the ladder, muttering to herself, and then she crawls into sight, and she has the popcorn popper all right—the electric one, with the plug dragging along the roof behind her. Sometimes I worry about that girl.

Anyway, I didn't have to go through all that because when we climb down, my neighbor, Lysolla Tideybole, is standing there and says she saw them birdies on the roof because she is a dedicated bird-watcher and she already called her girlfriend at the Louisiana Nature Center to come take care of them. Then she stares at the electric popper in my hands. I don't know what she is thinking.

I find out a week later. Our cat, Minny (he is a boy

but he don't know Minny is a girl's name), rubs up against Gumdrop's bedroom wall, which she is painting Pepto-Bismol pink, so we have a Pepto-Bismol pink cat. It is water-soluble paint, thank God. But I am going to have to give him a bath. And he is going to try to decapitate me when I do it.

I go outside, where we keep our big old crawfish boiler, which is good for a lot of things the directions don't mention. I put just enough water in so it ain't going to be over Minny's head, and I heat up that water on the outside burner and test it with my elbow. When it is nice and warm, I turn off the fire and dump in some bubble bath. I drop Minny in, and slam down the lid and hold it down. I can hear him churning around in there plenty, trying to claw his way out, which is good because he is agitating the water like a washing machine. And I am still holding that lid down when Lysolla storms in with the police. She has told them I am boiling my cat.

Well, it takes a lot of explaining because that cat is so mad you'd think he was boiled, but I finally convince them that I am not no satanist, and I wasn't trying to fry baby birds on my roof last week.

Maybe Sister Gargantua was right about following directions.

It's the Thought That Counts (Not the Smell)

~~~~~~~~~

"Peace on earth to men of good will." Ain't that the truth. Peace to men. Women sure don't get no peace at Christmas. Every day after work I am rushing around discount houses while my husband Lout is home on the couch, full of goodwill and beer, watching the Charlie Brown holiday special.

And it ain't enough that I got to buy presents for just me to give, but I also got to get presents for other people to give—things for Lout to give to his boss and for my kids to give all their teachers and also their little friends.

And look at the trash I get back. For the second year in a row Lout come home with this tin Santa Claus cannister full of popcorn from his friend Railbird. The thing is so big it comes up to my knee, but last year him and his brothers emptied it out completely watching the Sugar Bowl and I am stuck with a cannister I got no use for. Finally I come up with the idea of dumping the used cat litter in there instead of hauling it out every day after the cat has done his busines. The lid closes tight, so you can't smell nothing, and I can get away with not emptying it for a week. But now I got another cannister, which will probably be empty after this year's Sugar Bowl and I ain't getting another cat to keep that full.

I think it is better to give something small that don't last forever. Like what my kids usually give their teachers. It is a ceramic apple that has "Merry Xmas" on it in neon green. It don't take up much space and when you get sick of it you can accidentally knock it off the desk and break it. My mother-in-law Miss Larda, she makes a bunch of them every year. She is real talented like that. She makes things for other people too. She did a cute little foot with a red bunion for the mailman, and a tooth for her dentist, with a brown spot in the middle to look like a cavity.

But this year we had a disaster. It is three days before Christmas, and Miss Larda is just putting the finishing touches on her apples, which are all in rows on her card table. Then Lout walks in with his brand-new bowling ball, takes it out the case to show her, sets it on the table, and turns around to get a beer. Well, either the table or the floor ain't level because the bowling ball takes off like Godzilla and squashes all them little Merry Christmas apples to smithereens. All she got left is her foot and tooth, which she had set off to the side.

By now it is really too late to make more apples,

and even if it wasn't she is too mad to do it and I don't blame her. But I am stuck with no presents for all these teachers. And this is the year Gumdrop got Sister Mephistophela, the world's meanest math teacher, and she figures she got to give her something good. Plus she says she got to give something to all her best friends and she got thirty-eight of them. So what'm I going to do?

Thank God we live in New Orleans, is all I can say. The next day, I take the kids down to one of them stores where they sell that stuff for people to throw to the crowd from Mardi Gras floats, and for prizes in claw machines like they got in bowling alleys: little bitty stuffed animals and backscratchers shaped like hands with long fingernails and clear plastic paperweights with a figure of Elvis in the snow inside. All kinds of nice little gifts you can buy by the dozen for next to nothing. So we all go home happy, and the next day the kids bring their presents to school.

And I think it is fine until that night, when I tell Gumdrop to empty out the cat litter. And she opens up the cannister and she lets out a shriek. It is full of popcorn, she tells me. That don't make no sense until she finally explains she decided the backscratcher wasn't a good enough present for Sister Mephistophela so she grabbed the Santa Claus cannister and gave it to her instead. But it looks like what Sister got was a couple gallons of used cat litter.

"She didn't jump back when she opened it up?" I

ask. But Gumdrop is weeping and wailing and she says, "She didn't open it. She said she was going to bring it to the faculty Christmas party and share it."

Well, that Christmas party didn't last too long. I find out about it from my friend Awlette because her sister is a teacher at the school. Everybody cleared out pretty fast after old Mephistophela plunked her contribution on the table and yanked it open, she tells me.

But luck is on our side, because Sister Mephistophela don't ever bother to keep track of who gives her what. She usually just passes out a mimeographed note to all her students that says, "To those of you who gave gifts, thank you for your kindness. I will pray for each and every one of your intentions at Holy Mass." This year the note also said, "And I will pray for that person who needs forgiveness. YOU know who you are."

Well, Gumdrop knows who she is all right, but Sister Mephistophela don't. So we all had a Merry Christmas. Merry Christmas to you too. And peace to everybody.

The Thrill of
Boredom

~~~~~~~~~~

You know how you are always hearing about how boring it is to be a housewife? Well, I spent three years waiting around for some boredom. I didn't ask much. I would have settled for just a couple hours. A half hour even. I never got it.

It was a big disappointment, I can tell you. I have had a job since I got out of school, but it wasn't so my life wouldn't be empty. It was so my stomach wouldn't be empty. I know there are people going around saying stuff like today's woman needs to have it all. All what? All the work, that's what they mean. Take that commercial where that poor lady brings home the bacon and fries it up in the pan. I want to know who scrubs out that pan and puts it away. You notice they don't sing about that. God knows when she gets to sit down. Well, I for one can do without it all. Just let me sit.

Anyway, that's what I always said. But that was before I got my wish. It happened when the place I worked at, Fine Art's Seafood, ran into trouble with the board of health, and Fine Art went back to selling shrimp out a ice chest on Highway 90.

By a miracle, that same week, my husband Lout gets promoted to head mechanic at the bowling alley and he also gets a nice little raise. So I decide to be a lady of leisure for a while. And I run right out and buy a three-pound box of chocolate-covered cherries to nibble on while I watch the soaps.

But things start to change in our family once Lout is on the fast track. When we both had jobs, Lout would drop off the older kids at school on his way to work, and they didn't have no choice but to be ready when he was ready to leave. But now he has to get there at the crack of dawn, and it is up to me to get them to school. And now they don't see why they can't drag around until the last minute.

There are a lot of other ladies of leisure with raincoats thrown over their nightgowns who drop off their kids at the last minute too. And they got their own code of rules. The object is to eject each kid right at the school gate in a minimum number of seconds so the next mother can pull up and eject her kid. You don't break the code. You never, for instance, kiss your kid good-bye. Picture twenty-five mothers gunning their motors in front the school, twenty-five carloads of kids whining that they are going to get tardy slips. Then the kid who is at the gate stops, turns around, and leans back into the car to kiss his Mama. Them other twenty-four mothers go berserk. They honk, they shake their fists, and two or three of them start cutting U-turns on the school lawn. You better get that kid kissed up before you leave home in the morning if you want to survive.

Also, you should write all notes to the teacher and sign all your kids' test papers ahead of time. Of course, the kid is not going to tell you he needs a note until he is at the school gate. And then you scribble down something in crayon on your knee in five seconds while rioting breaks out in the line behind you, and you shove it at him through the window, and he stands there and looks at it and then says Sister Mary Beth will not think that is neat enough, and will you rewrite it please.

This is how my day starts. I get back home and go to stick my cold cup of coffee in the microwave, and the breakfast dishes are still on the table and the house is a mess. It was like that when I had my job, but I wasn't around to look at it.

Then the baby, who sleeps like a angel on the trip to school, comes alive and starts her little daily routine: stab at the electric socket with the car keys, root around a little in the kitty litter, pull all the disposable diapers out the box and drop them in the toilet. She always keeps one mess ahead of me. Finally she crawls in the cabinet underneath the kitchen sink and curls up for a nap while I get hysterical looking for her. Just when I find her and dump her in her crib, my mother-in-law, Miss Larda, strolls in and tells me I should lock my doors because I never know who is going to get in. That is true, because here she is.

She goes over to my stove to drip some coffee the way God meant it to be dripped, and sits down to talk at me while I clean up. And I am so starved for conversation from anybody over the age of puberty, I am glad to listen. Then Lout phones and says since I don't got nothing to do, can I run to McDonald's and pick him up a couple Quarter-Pounders with cheese.

And when I get back from that, the phone is ringing and it is the school. They need somebody to blow the insides out of a couple thousand eggs and fill them with confetti for the fair. Or it is the school nurse telling me my little nephew Locust is sick to his stomach, and would I come get him to throw up at my house because his Mama is a working woman and can't leave her job. That's how my days go.

Anyway, even with the promotion, pretty soon we got more bills than money, and I am looking for another career opportunity. When a position opens up behind the fine jewelry and trophy counter at the bowling alley, I jump at it.

Them chocolate cherries got freezer burn, and I finally had to feed them to the dog. He is a lot more bored than I ever was.

The Agony of the Armpits

~~~~~~~~~~

I don't want to be blasphemous or nothing, but sometimes you got to wonder what God was thinking about, letting us evolve like we did. For instance, other animals got fur all over them. We don't, except in certain very important places which need special protection. Like our armpits.

Now why, I want to know, was God so worried about our armpits? I can understand why we got hair on top of our heads—to keep our brains from baking in the sun. But we don't got brains in our armpits. And I can understand why various other unmentionable places would need to be covered up by hair. But armpits? Even in a Catholic school, a armpit ain't considered a object of lust.

Now my sister-in-law Gloriosa, she is one of them modern thinkers, and she says women should make a statement by simply not shaving. I thought about that, but I ain't going to make no statement with my armpits.

It's a strange world. Men shave their faces and women shave under their arms and their legs. How much of your legs you shave depends on how old you are. My mother-in-law Miss Larda, she shaves from her ankles to just underneath her kneecaps. She says she ain't showing more than that, so she ain't shaving more than that. I shave up to where my shorts end. My daughter Gumdrop, she spends her summers at the lakefront in a high-cut bathing suit, and she shaves A LOT. She got razor scars in places which I was brought up to believe it was a sin to even think about.

Gloriosa says in Europe women don't have this problem because they never touch a razor to their bodies. Ain't that something. Think about it. Queen Elizabeth in her thousand-dollar designer dress and her crown and scepter and a pair of legs like bottle brushes. Maybe that's why she spends so much time waving off balconies that got flags draped over the railings. Keeping them hairy legs out of sight.

But in New Orleans, your legs and armpits are supposed to be bald, whether you are the Queen of England or not. So you do what you got to do.

The problem with shaving is generally you do it just before you go someplace real important. So when you cut yourself, you got not only the pain of a cut with soap in it, but you also know you are about to look like a fool.

It don't matter if you are a man in a tie, or a woman with your good high heels on. Somebody is going to ooze over to you and smirk and say, "Whoops. Cut yourself shaving. Heh. Heh." They don't never ask if maybe you fought your way through a barbed-wire fence or something. They always know. You might as well just stick some toilet paper on the bottom of your shoe and let that trail around, to complete your image.

Which is why probably men grow beards. If you are a woman, you look for alternative methods. Around the time you are fourteen or fifteen, you spend your allowance on some goop that is supposed to make them hairs disappear like magic. You take it home and you slather it on, and then, while you are waiting for it to work, you get around to reading the directions, which say DO NOT let it touch your eyes or vital organs and don't drip it on no furniture or your mother's carpet and REMOVE IMMEDIATELY after twenty minutes or they won't be responsible for what happens. So there you are with your legs hanging over the bathtub, staring at the soap dish and wondering if they got this stuff out of some toxic waste dump somewhere and maybe it has numbed your legs and is eating them to the bone, like piranhas. Finally, the twenty minutes is up and you wash it off real fast. Your legs are not eaten. Neither are your hairs. Every one of them is still there, shiny clean.

Of course, if you have the money, you can pay for something that will just yank your hairs out by the roots. Gumdrop bought a little hand-held invention which is supposed to do this. She runs it over about three inches of her thigh before she realizes that removing hairs by yanking involves pain. She and I are arguing about whether she can get her money back or not, when my husband Lout walks in. He don't believe in wasting money, and he says probably Gumdrop just been using this thing wrong. He picks it up and says, "Now, watch this."

Like usual, Lout is wearing blue jeans and his sleeveless undershirt. So instead of running it up his leg, he sticks it in his armpit. It takes him about two seconds to realize this was a mistake. He just stands there with tears in his eyes awhile, and sort of squeaks, and then he runs into the bathroom. I follow him, because I know, of course, he got it caught. I got to cut him loose with the toenail scissors. Finally, he can put his arm down again, but he looks funny. I got to explain. Lout grows hair in all the same places Smokey the Bear grows hair. So when all the hair disappears out of one armpit it looks conspicuous, like he got mange. I have to run out and get him some T-shirts with sleeves. He says they make him look like a wimp. But he wears them for the rest of the summer.

Maybe Queen Elizabeth has the right idea.

Don't Poop on My Parade

~~~~~~~~~~

M y husband Lout says he ain't had much use for Mardi Gras ever since he was in his high school band and marched a entire parade route with his fly hanging open.

But me, I'm just the opposite. I can't wait for Christmas to be over so we can get to the Mardi Gras season. Christmas you got to pay for. Mardi Gras is free. Oh, you got to do a little screeching, maybe stomp a few fingers, but that ain't no worse than Christmas shopping, and it don't cost nothing.

This year our family's haul is going to be bigger than ever. Lout's brother Leech has a pickup truck. He got this job with the department of streets, and he needs the truck for all his equipment. Lout has his own pickup, but he thinks it is too precious for the only thing a pickup is good for, if you ask me. Catching things at parades.

Thank God Leech and the rest of the Gunches

think like me. Most years, we all go to the downtown parades. But in a pickup, you do better at the parades in a suburb, like Chalmette, where you can pull off the road and back up right to the curb. Then you just set up your lawn chairs in the truck bed, and gather up them beads as they rain down around you. We are even thinking of putting up a bull's-eye with a bag right underneath, so the float riders can aim at that. Most of the Chalmette parades are at night, so they might not be able to see it too good, but Leech was saying he could string Christmas lights around it.

Even without this, we catch plenty. And it is all free. This is the secret of Mardi Gras. As long as it's free, it's fun. But you mess it up if you start thinking how much better it would be if you was IN one of these parades. Do that, and Mardi Gras ain't free no more. It turns into work.

I myself played the cymbals in the Penguin Band back at Celibacy Academy High School. This means I get to walk five miles in a tall fur hat with a chin strap, clanging once every three blocks, while that dance team, the Prancing Penguinettes, gets all the attention. This is something I try to forget.

I guess I tried too hard, because when my daughter Gumdrop gets a chance to be in a parade, I don't object. Her dancing school is invited to perform in a parade in Chalmette wearing their dance review costumes. The theme of the dance review is Fuzzy Easter Friends, and

Gumdrop is so thrilled about the idea of tap-dancing through Chalmette dressed like a chicken, I don't have the heart to tell her no.

My mother-in-law, Miss Larda, is thrilled too. She gets Leech to haul everybody out there two hours early so she can choose a spot for a good photo opportunity. Then we all sit and wait until the parade starts. And wouldn't you know, when the first bunch of horses comes by, one of them leaves a horsey souvenir in the street. There is a rear end guard that is supposed to scoop it up, but they miss it. This is the kind of thing that gets Miss Larda very worried.

Then the first band comes along. They are all licking their lips and concentrating, just getting ready to strike up a song, when Miss Larda bellows out real loud, "WATCH YOU DON'T STEP IN THAT!" Well. Everybody in the band hears her, and everybody knows exactly what she means, but nobody knows where not to step. Most of them can't even see their feet for their instruments. Still and all, they react instantly. Some leap to the left and crash into the ones that decided to leap to the right; some jump backwards, and a few just lunge straight up and over what they think must be right in front of them. The effect is like one of them real complicated band dance routines being done by drunkards.

Miss Larda bellows again when the next marching group comes by, and she sends them into the same kind of panic. And she does it to the next group. And I know I got to act fast, because Gumdrop's tap-dancing chickens ain't going to be up to this.

And then I remember about Leech's street equipment, which he has shoved back out the way. I dig out one of them fluorescent orange traffic cones. Just before the next marchers get there, I give Leech a shove and he runs out and plunks it down in front the spot. And it works like a charm. The marchers just split up and flow around it. After they pass, he picks it up so the float behind won't hit it. He holds it upside down over his shoulder and the float riders see it glowing in the dark, and they go wild throwing stuff down it. It is better than a lighted-up bull's-eye.

After the float passes, Leech puts the cone back in the street. The next group is the dancing chickens, and Miss Larda grabs up her camera and yells, "GUM-DROP!" Gumdrop turns her head, and dances right into that orange cone. And I am thinking, we saved all them marchers from disaster and Gumdrop is going to fall right in. But them dancing lessons paid off, because she does this quick twirl and saves herself. Everybody along the curb claps, and she takes a little bow. Miss Larda snaps the picture, and she gets a extra copy for me. It is so precious. And free. If that ain't the spirit of Mardi Gras, I don't know what is.

Lout's Quantum Leap

~~~~~~~~~~

I t's that gorgeous time of year again. Flowers are blooming; butterflies are flittering; little birdies are popping out their eggs; the kids are outside in the sunshine and I am alone with the channel changer.

I should be ecstatic as a roach in a puddle of beer. Only one thing ruins it. This is the month we start with Daylight Savings Time. We all got to Spring Forward, they tell us. And I just ain't up to springing.

It's no problem in October, when we get that extra hour in the middle of the night. I just leave the alarm clock set for the regular time, so I can reach over and slam it off and Fall Backward onto the pillow. What good is a extra hour of sleep, if you don't wake up to enjoy it? But Springing Forward is a whole other story. Whichever government people make up these things think that since they gave us the extra hour while we was sleeping, they got to take it away at the same time. Like that makes sense. Any ninny could find a better hour to get rid of than one that comes before dawn.

I think they should take that hour out of a Friday afternoon. Just imagine. Here you are at four in the afternoon, dragging around, sick and tired of work. Bing. It is now five o'clock, and you pick up your purse and go home. This would make things easier on everybody.

My husband Lout says it would be a lot easier on him. He says the way things are, he is groggy all summer long. He says he just don't feel right until fall, when he gets back that hour's sleep he lost. I don't notice no difference in him myself. I think he is groggy 365 days a year. But I don't say nothing.

Anyway, it is true that this Springing Forward business makes trouble for everybody. Especially if you are not what they call a morning person. I don't personally know any morning people and I am not sure there is such a thing. Anybody who makes a habit out of humming and whistling and telling knock-knock jokes before breakfast probably gets killed young.

A normal person just goes on automatic pilot that time of day. Put one foot out the bed. Stop and think. Put the other foot out the bed. Stop and think. Go in the bathroom. Come out the bathroom. Find the kitchen. Plug in the coffee. Drink the coffee. Go back in the bathroom. Come out the bathroom.

About the time I reach this point, I have remembered I got kids. I take a deep breath, and wake them up.

On a ordinary day, they will sit up in bed, blink,

and then yell that they are LATE and one of their shoes is gone and their socks don't match and somebody went in their dresser and took their last pair of clean drawers and their brother drank the last swig of milk right out the bottle. After a half hour of rioting, they shoot out the house, one after the other, like machine gun bullets, and forget their homework.

Now. You push all that back a hour, like for the first week after Daylight Savings Time starts, and you make everybody a hour tireder and a hour grouchier, and you are not talking about just regular rioting. You are talking about Mardi Gras in Hell.

Of course what happened to us last spring took the cake. On Saturday night, just before we haul ourselves into the bed, Lout goes around the house resetting all the clocks, just like they tell you to do on TV. But he miscalculates and sets them a hour back instead of a hour forward.

The next day I get out of bed, and I don't feel at all sleepy, so I figure I must be living healthy or something. I don't know I am now two hours behind everybody in the entire time zone.

But that afternoon, Lout settles back with his beer and pork skins to watch a ball game, and when he turns it on, they are already into the seventh inning stretch. So he calls the TV station and puts on this real snotty superior tone, and informs them that it is scheduling improprieties like this that drive people to cable TV. It would of been bad enough if the lady who answered the phone just thought he was crazy. But she knows his kind. She outsnots him. "Sir, our schedule is correct," she says. "Did you set your clocks back instead of forward, sir?" So much for the wind in his sails.

Then we realize the worst. My mother-in-law, Miss Larda, is boiling crawfish at her house, and all the relatives are supposed to be there at three. Now if this was a baby shower or a stuffed-up toilet or her cat was in a tree, Miss Larda would have been on the phone in five seconds to find out why we wasn't there. But a crawfish boil is different. If you aren't pushed up to the table at starting time, there's that much more for everybody else. It is now four, and by the time we rush in, they are just sitting around belching and all that's left on the table is shells and wet newspaper.

We wind up going to McDonald's.

And that's why I ain't fond of spring.

Gunches Bustin' Out
All Over

~~~~~~~~~~

W ho wrote the song that goes "Summertime, and the living is easy"? Must have been some nun. They don't have to worry with kids underfoot for three months.

This is one time of year I appreciate my mother-in-law. She lets all the grandchildren go by her house all summer. Which means me and my sister-in-law Larva can keep our jobs. Last year my husband Lout, he says we got to get something really nice for his Mama to show her how grateful we are. I am thinking maybe a box of Goo-Goo Clusters and a six-pack, but he says, "Let's all pitch in and build her a swimming pool."

Well. I know he got mixed motives for that. Lout always tells me the only way to get through summer is to move into a air-conditioned bar or stay underwater for four months. So I guess his tab at the Sloth Lounge must be running up and he is looking at the alternatives.

Still, it ain't a bad idea. A pool would get the kids

out from in front the TV for a while. And the adults would go for it too. All my in-laws love the water. Of course (except for Gloriosa, the family beauty), none of them can fit into a bathing suit smaller than a size 44 wide. So they sure can float good.

Anyway, we all decide it is a good idea. Of course, we don't got the budget for no luxury Olympic pool, but we figure we can get a nice four-foot above-ground round one and set it up ourselves. And it costs even less than we thought, because Lout goes to a garage sale and finds one that somebody used for a few years and then took down. So he hauls all the pieces into Miss Larda's backyard, and we all get out there and scream at each other for a few hours while we we get it set up. It ain't no worse than decorating our truck for Mardi Gras.

And the next Sunday we all go over there with our bathing suits and goggles and frog fins. My mother-in-law, Miss Larda, is all dressed up in this green muumuu with palm trees and pictures of volcanoes all over it, and she says she is going to stay dry and barbecue some chickens. First the kids swim, and then we feed them lunch and tell them they can't go swimming for an hour or they will get cramps, and we send them inside. Then it is the grown-ups' turn, while Miss Larda puts on another batch of chickens.

I should have realized that a whole herd of adult Gunches would be too much for any swimming pool, especially a secondhand one. But I don't think of that. So everybody starts having a good time, just like they do in them drink commercials. Lurch is on his back with a beer in his hand and a palm branch in his navel pretending he is a desert island. Larva has on her swim cap with the yellow and orange rubber flower petals and she is floating along on her stomach, like a hippopotamus in a Sunday hat. I am working on syncronized swimming myself, trying to do the backstroke and stick one leg up.

Then Leech and Lout decide to jump in at the same time from opposite sides of the pool. One of them yells "Timber!" and the other one yells "Geronimo!" but what happens next is more like the fury of Hurricane Betsy.

I guess if close to 600 pounds of blubber crashed into a in-ground pool, the water would just splash up and out. But what happens to us is the seam in the pool wall rips opens, and all the water and all the Gunches and me get sucked under and spat out into the yard, like ants in the nozzle of a garden hose. It is quite a shock. One minute I am floating along very graceful, pointing my toe up in the air and the next minute I am flat on my back in the wet grass. I sit up and look around and I see Gunches splayed out all over the yard. Lurch is still clutching his can of beer, but I know it got to be half water by now. Leech has landed in Miss Larda's banana tree and he has decided to stay there because his bathing trunks evidently got hung up on the side of the pool when we all came shooting out. He is using a bunch of baby bananas for modesty. Larva, poor thing, washed up under the porch and she comes scrabbling out on all fours because the dog uses that as his summer home and don't like sudden visitors.

Miss Larda is standing there with a soaking-wet muumuu clinging to all parts of her, so she looks like several of them volcanic islands. And the barbecue pit and all the chicken has been swooshed clear down to the K and B Drugstore on the corner.

And that was the end of the Gunch swimming party. The next day Miss Larda buys a little two-foot-high pool for the kids to play in. She says if she hears any large persons whining about being hot, she'll turn her hose on them. Lout, Leech, and Lurch go back to beating the heat at the Sloth Lounge.

So much for summertime when the living is easy. And I'll say THAT to any singing nun who tries to tell me different.

Memories of an Old Flame and Setting the School on Fire

~~~~~~~~~

A week before I graduate from Celibacy Academy, my teacher, Sister Gargantua, gets sentimental. She stands up in front of the class of '66 with her eyes all watery and she tells us, "Girls, appreciate this time of your life. You are in the fullness of your youth and at the peak of your beauty."

It was the worst thing she could have said.

I am seventeen years old. I got zits, I got braces, I got hair like Phyllis Diller and the figure of a mop. And this is my peak? This is all there is? I get so upset I eat seventeen chocolate Moon Pies and a Goo-Goo Cluster, and my face breaks out so bad I could scare the dog.

I tell you, you got to be careful what you say to teenagers. They get depressed easy. I am always careful to come up with positive stuff. Like, "Now, Sweetness, in a few years from now if you watch what you eat that skin will clear up and you'll catch yourself a decent boyfriend." Or "Kid, you got nowhere to go but up." Something cheerful.

Of course these teenagers today are smarter than we was. It don't matter what they look like. They just say it is the style. Split ends? Uh-uh. That's a punk hair-do. Better yet, shave your head. Splotches on your face? Paint your face white with a black bat across it and who will notice? That group KISS probably never would have started all their foolishness if they had good complexions.

But back in 1966, we was a lot more oppressed than they are today. Celibacy Academy was like a all-girl boot camp, and no male human who wasn't a relative or a elderly priest was allowed anywhere near the premises. Unless it was for a school dance.

School dances was mandatory. I guess the nuns figured a few of us was going to have to propagate the species one day, so we might as well learn to dance. All the dances was in the gym and we had to introduce whatever date we had managed to dig up to the nuns, and at the same time be inspected in our evening gowns. Those gowns were not to be low-cut enough to reveal cleavage. I would have given anything if I had any cleavage to reveal. Or any date to introduce until senior year, when I finally met my future husband Lout.

On the good side, all this plus the fact we thought everything was a sin pretty much kept us out of trouble. Once a week we would all file into the school chapel, St. Scrupula's, home of the world's dullest confessions. We

would ask for absolution for things like disgracing our
Celibacy uniform by rolling up the sleeves on our school
blouses or shaving our legs above our kneecaps. The
only time I had anything good to confess was the time
I almost burned the church down.

I got to explain. Celibacy Academy was big on tra-
ditions, and one of them was for the seniors to gather in
the big entry alcove to St. Scrupula's and light four
candles in a flowered wreath, while the class goody-
goodies took turns reciting the highlights of each of our
four high school years. The ones who weren't goody-
goodies got to participate by mopping the alcove ahead
of time, or something like that. My friend Awlette and
myself got the job of setting up the wreath.

Now Awlette, she was always creative. Every other
class just plopped the wreath on top the marble holy
water font that stood by itself in the middle of the
alcove. But Awlette, she wants to suspend it from
above. So that morning, we sneak Lout into the chapel,
and he hammers four white ribbons to the arch over the
font, and ceiling, and ties the other ends to the wreath.
Then we hand him up the four candles, and he sticks
one next to each ribbon.

Lout has never been inside Celibacy Academy
before, and he wants to hang around and see what he
can see. When he's done, he goes and crouches in a
shadowy corner, thinking he can keep his 250 pounds
out of sight. Pretty soon Sister Gargantua leads the class
in and we start up the ceremony. I pick up the big long

candlelighter and light the first candle. The candle immediately lights the ribbon, and the flame races up toward St. Scrupula's ceiling.

Awlette rushes over to the holy water font and cups her hands and starts scooping handfuls of holy water on the fire. But it don't do no good. We are going to be Celibacy Academy's last senior class, I am thinking, because we are burning the place down.

Then Lout leaps into action. He grabs the fire extinguisher off the wall next to him, turns it on, and rushes into the crowd holding it out in front of him with both hands and the hose whirling around over his head, spraying foam every which way. Everybody is so much in shock from seeing a MAN they don't think to jump for cover until they got a few coats of foam on them. Finally Lout manages to aim the hose at the fire. It fizzles out quick, but Sister Gargantua don't. I ain't going to go into what she said, only it wasn't sentimental.

I think Lout is a hero.

Afterwards, he told me I could light his fire anytime.

And you know, I never told that in confession.

Sveating to Be Svelte

~~~~~~~~

W hat I want to know is why people like my sister-in-law Larva pay good money to belong to some spa so they can steam theirselves in a sauna when they can get exactly the same effect if they plop down in front their house any day in summer. Of course, in the spas they can plop stark naked. Maybe that's the attraction.

If steam really made people lose weight, New Orleans, which ain't nothing but one huge steam cabinet four months a year, would be the home of the skinniest people on the face of the earth. And if steam was good for complexions, we would all have skin like Georgia peaches. New Orleans would be the beautiful people capital of America. But I look around and I know that sure ain't the truth.

And even if steam did make our bodies gorgeous, it don't exactly fill us up with pep and energy. There ain't no such thing as a brisk after-dinner walk in New Orleans, because there ain't no such thing as brisk. Around here we just sit around after dinner and belch. Even dinner is generally something we don't have to chew but every once in a while, like gumbo and watermelon.

Of course, this ain't just true for New Orleans. It is like this in Florida and Mississippi and everywhere else cold-blooded creatures like alligators and lizards and turtles, which crawl around naked and hate to jog, have decided to call home. Evidently Ponce de León and Bienville and them other founding fathers who decided two-legged, fashion-conscious human beings should move in here, didn't see the implications of that.

Nonreptiles got fashion problems here. You can't never dress for the weather. Willard Scott says it's going to be 95 degrees, so naturally you strip down to as little as you can and still be decent. Then you walk into the supermarket or the bowling alley or the mall, and they got the air conditioner turned to "blizzard" and your sweat freezes right in your armpits. Of course, if you left home wearing what you need to survive in them temperatures, like your thermal underwear and your hooded parka, you would be boiled like a shrimp before you got six steps down the front walk.

My husband Lout don't have this problem because he got natural insulation, like whales do. No matter where he is, he struts around in his flip-flops and sleeveless undershirt. Now, Lout ain't no Arnold Schwarzenegger. He got squishy lumps and bumps and tufts of hair shooting out here and there, and in his sleeveless undershirt, he got the sex appeal of a pot scrubber. But I don't say nothing. Any little floozie thinking about making a play for Lout has the right to see him in all his glory. I call that security.

What gets me is how Lout and all these other men who walk around resting their beer cans on their bellies think they got a right to make WOOF-WOOF noises if a woman walks by with a couple extra ounces of cellulite exposed.

And poor Larva, who got a couple hundred pounds of cellulite, she takes this kind of criticism serious. She is determined to sweat off her fat, and sitting in the spa just ain't working fast enough.

Then she sees a TV commercial for this instant weight-loss garment that you have to rush to order from operators that they got standing by. They call it a Sauna Svelte Suit, and the commercial guarantees that she will lose pounds and inches in mere hours. So she rushes to order it. Well, this Svelte Suit turns out to be black rubber underwear which covers her from her bosom to her knees. The directions tell her to powder herself down and wrestle herself into it. Well, she figures, that should work off a few hundred calories right there.

But then she is supposed to simply slip her everyday clothes over it and proceed with her normal daily activities. No activities are normal with rubber underwear on, I'll tell you that. For one thing, she squeaks pretty loud when she moves. So here she is trying to get her groceries at Schwegmann's with sound effects like a rusty hinge (or even worse if you ain't thinking polite) and people are staring at her like she needs a squirt of WD-40.

Then, when she starts to heat up, she gives off a aroma like her radiator hose got a hole in it.

Finally, she can't stand it no more and she ducks into the Schwegmann's ladies room and rolls the thing off of her. Then she don't know what to do with it. So she drops it into the discount meat case and says a little prayer for whoever tries to cook it for supper.

Maybe they'll steam it.

Siblings in the
Snake Pit

~~~~~~~~~

T hey say big families with lots of kids is going the
way of the dinosaurs. Well, if that's true, them
kids got nobody but theirselves to blame. They
are a lot of work.

I only got three myself, thank God. I myself was
raised in a family with eight kids. We celebrated like it
was Mardi Gras whenever somebody got potty trained.

My little daughter Gumdrop wants her own bedroom. I never had a room of my own and I would have
to divorce my husband to get one now. But I don't have
to sleep in a bunk bed no more, so I ain't complaining.

I remember we all wanted the top bunks, so we
made a rule that you wasn't old enough to get one until
you could climb into it without a ladder, even if that
meant you had to step on the bottom bunk and your
little sister's face to do it. If the face happened to belong
to my sister Chlorine, she would get even by playing
"virgin in a volcano." You was the virgin and she would

use her feet to make a volcano rise up in the middle of your mattress until you appeased her with a old Easter egg or whatever you had stashed under your pillow in case of emergency.

We had one bathroom, and if it was full—that didn't mean if there was just one person in there, that meant if each of the fixtures was being used at the moment—we ran out and used the toilet in the garage, or else the hose in the backyard, depending on what we needed to do. And I never stepped into a bathtub that didn't already have a couple sisters in it until I was eleven years old.

I read in the papers where today's average kid watches 8.6 acts of television violence per week. Well, we sure didn't watch no violent acts, I can tell you that. We did them ourselves.

I remember the time my brother Vizine had signed up for Sister Louis Augustine's flute class after school. Vizine was the one with talent. He got bored with playing the flute the regular way, so he decided to play it with his nose. This was a big accomplishment because it got him a lot of attention, got Sister Louis Augustine sick to her stomach, and kept anybody from borrowing his flute. But he had to practice a lot to get it right.

My sister Adrenaleen hated this. She was the oldest and the meanest, so when Adrenaleen talked, everybody listened. Most of the time. But this time Vizine decided his music was more important than the fear of Adrenaleen. So here she is, flopped across a top bunk trying to study, and Vizine starts up playing "When the Saints Go Marching In." She yells at him to stop, but he goes right into the second verse: "Oh, when the sun begins to shine . . ." She says she will put that flute where the sun don't shine. He still don't stop. Finally, she climbs down and tears across the hall to the boys' bedroom. The door is locked, and the music is louder than ever. She bangs on the door, and then she backs off and smashes it open, ready for blood. But Vizine ain't there. There is just the flute, all by itself, laying quietly on Vizine's pillow. But she can still hear the last notes trailing off. Then the whole song starts over. Turns out he had made a tape recording, and he snuck in the attic and put the tape recorder right over her room, turned it on full blast, and went off to shoot some baskets.

And of course we had automobile violence. Each of the kids' main goal in life was to sit in the front seat by the window. It was a obsession. When Vizine was thirteen and my father drove him on his first date he had to warn him ahead of time that it was not considered sophisticated to shout, "Front seat!" and shove the girl aside and dive in the front window.

But there was some good points about riding in back. When we passed a eighteen-wheeler we would all signal for the driver to blare his air horn, so we could watch my father jump out his skin.

And every time we came to a stop light, we could see the people in the next cars saying, "How many kids they got in there?" and start counting us. Just to confuse them, we would get the little ones, Bovine and Praline, to lay down on the floor, and then pop up one at a time while Vazeline and Chlorine got down, and we would keep that up until the light changed.

Whenever we took a trip across the lake or somewhere, Mama would put all the backseats down in the station wagon and spread quilts and pillows around and tell us to be nice and quiet and go to sleep. After a while I got to be very comfortable sleeping in a pile with brothers and sisters squirming all around. To this day, I think I could take a nap in a snake pit.

Well, the last snake has grown up and left the pit, and I got to talking to Mama the other day about how she managed all them kids. She says to me, "You got three kids. How busy are you?" I says, "Are you kidding? I am running twenty-four hours a day." She says, "Well, there ain't no more than twenty-four hours in the day. So go ahead and have all the kids you want. You can't get no busier."

It's that kind of thinking which could bring back the dinosaurs, if we ain't careful.

How to Tie One On

~~~~~~~~

During the olden days, like in the Bible, people got dressed by taking big pieces of cloth and tying them on. They would just throw some cloth over their shoulder and tie a rope around their waist for a toga, and then they might tie another piece around their neck for a cape, and maybe another piece around their head to be fancy. So when they were getting dressed up, they tied two or three pieces of cloth on. But when they wasn't feeling so good, like maybe after one of them orgies they used to throw back then, they only tied one of them on. That's where we get the expression today, "tying one on."

Anyway, the system worked fine, for a while. And then this man thought up the sewing machine. He probably got worn out keeping his wife barefoot and pregnant, and he figured this would keep her just as frazzled.

It worked. Sewing machines can turn calm, cheerful women into hysterical lunatics, just because of all them ridiculous details you got to remember. Like never lay out a pattern to cut on the floor if you got a kid that ain't 100 percent potty trained. And even if you spend a month creating a gorgeous formal for some dance, you can be embarrassed for life by one little mistake that you don't know about until you are at the dance. Like putting them little pointy darts that are supposed to flatter your bosom in the back, where you ain't got no bosom.

Of course some women sail right through stuff like that. They thrive on it. They hang around Cloth World like men hang around hardware stores, only instead of fondling bolt clippers and grout spreaders, they get frothed up over pinking shears and pin cushions shaped like tomatoes. You got to admire them. They can snatch up a couple scraps of nylon net and some satin and run up ensembles for a entire wedding party.

My mother-in-law is like that. And my husband Lout, poor heart, assumed it was the same with every woman. When we are first married, he tosses me his pants with the entire backside looking like it exploded and he says, "I need these tomorrow morning, Sugarboo." Well, I get the stapler and lay a solid line of metal in there and the next day I just hand him his pants and tell him to be very, very careful when he sits down. I got along like this for years. There ain't nothing you can do with a needle and thread that you can't do faster with staples and tape and dental floss. Except actually MAKE your clothes. But who needs to do that as long as we got clearance sales? The day Lout starts cutting the lawn with a sickle is the day I'll start making clothes. That's what I always said.

But of course, I live to regret it. See, usually at Halloween I throw together costumes for the kids with whatever is lying around. One year I had it all planned out ahead of time. Tie the toilet lid cover—it is one of them nice fluffy white ones—on my son Gargoyle and give him some fangs and whiskers and he is a wolf in sheep's clothing. For my daughter Gumdrop, stuff a big brown plastic leaf bag with inflated balloons. Put it on Gumdrop with just her head and feet showing. Then take a plastic flowered slipcover off one of my couch cusions and fill it with balloons, and tape it to her rear end. Ta-daaa—a couch potato. These costumes ain't what you see gracing Carnival balls, but they are plenty good enough to run around in the dark and yell trick or treat in.

But that year Halloween starts oozing into the daylight hours. The school decides to put on this big costume contest in the afternoon. Some kid's father, who owns a TV shop, actually offers to donate a VCR for first prize.

And now the pressure is on. Them sewing cult women go into a frenzy. They turn their kids into dragons with tongues that light up with battery packs, and killer bees with hand-starched stingers and Carnival satin crawfish with sequin-covered antennas.

I can see a toilet cover and a couch cushion ain't

going to cut it, but Gumdrop and Gargoyle are already talking about what movies they want to rent when they get their VCR.

I feel like a unfit mother. It ain't fair. If I got to feel this guilty, it ought to be for something good. Like maybe for carrying on in a sinful manner with Kevin Costner. That might be worth it. This ain't.

Anyway, the big day comes. They have even built a outdoor reviewing stand for the costume contest. They forget this is New Orleans, city of rain. Just before the contest starts, when all the kids are lined up behind the reviewing stand, it starts coming down cats and dogs.

Then just as fast as it starts, it stops. And all them pathetic little contestants trail across the stage, with their tongues short-circuited and their little stingers and antennas all drooping. Then the last costume comes out—the only one that still looks decent. The couch potato, which is 100 percent plastic.

After we bring home the VCR, I ask my mother-in-law to watch the kids and I go out with Lout and tie one on. He ain't no Kevin Costner, so I don't feel guilty about nothing.

Of Mice and Machismo

~~~~~~~~

I t's macho season again. This is the time of year
when real men sniff the air, flex their hairy arms,
thump their chests, and flop on the sofa to watch
football through January.

Or else they go hunting.

If you got a husband with a bad case of macho-
ness, you just as well get used to it. Either he is hunched
in front of the TV chug-a-lugging taco chips right out of
the bag and snorting in his beer, or he is clattering
around the house before dawn looking for his duck call
and going off dressed like a bush.

Last year, my husband, Lout, and his sister's husband, Fred, took up hunting. Fred's wife Larva was very
upset. She is a big woman with a big heart, and she just
loves little things like duckies and bunnies. But Fred
and Lout are leaving every weekend saying things like
"Beautiful day. What'll we kill?"

Of course, them two have never killed nothing except a couple flasks of whatever it is they sip to keep themselves warm. And while they are squatting in the swamp quacking, we can lounge around and let the kids live on McDonald's.

On the bad side, if a emergency arises, we got to handle it.

Now it ain't like I myself don't handle a lot of emergencies all year around. Any emergency that got to do with anything one of the kids meant to do in the bathroom but didn't get there fast enough, that is always my department, because my husband Lout, he ain't macho about them kind of things.

But there is one emergency I know I need Lout for. A car emergency. Because Lout can talk to the men at our garage.

Like I was telling Larva, if a woman explains to these garage men that this car will only go backward and makes this BREEP CRUSH CLONK noise, they just smirk at you like you are saying you have met the tooth fairy. They have decided in them ball-bearings they got for brains that there ain't nothing wrong with your car. You are doing this to waste their time. So they open up a couple beers and wait for you to call back in two days so they can say, "Looks fine to us, ma'am. Runs like a top."

But if Lout goes over there, he just strides up to them and hitches up his pants and rolls up on the balls of his feet, and right away they know they are talking to a real man and if he says the car's broke, then the car's broke. And they fix it.

So just to be on the safe side, when Lout goes off hunting, I use his pickup, which don't usually break down. (Lout and Fred go hunting in Fred's truck because it has one of them covers for the back that they can crawl under to sleep after they killed their limit in flasks. I won't let Lout buy one, because I want to use that pickup for what God intended pickups for—standing in to watch Mardi Gras parades—once I convince him I won't get no scratches in it with the bottoms of my feet.)

Anyway, last weekend I take Larva to the mall in the truck. She wants to comfort herself with a couple chocolate chip cookie cakes plus she wants to pick up a birthday present for her little boy, Locust. She don't mention that the present is a pair of little baby mice, which Larva says are "precious."

When we are ready to go home, Larva heaves herself up on the seat and then perches this little thin cardboard box of mice on her lap. I guess I get a little bit distracted, because I almost run a stop sign. I hit the brakes hard just in time and I also slam my right arm across Larva. (Before they made universal carseat laws, they used to give you a pill right after childbirth that fixed your brain waves so that, whenever you stopped short for the rest of your life, you would slam your arm across the person next to you, even if that person wasn't your kid.)

But I whomp the mouse box, and it pops open and them precious mice run right up my arm. Naturally, I do what anybody does when two mice run up their arm while they are driving. I throw open the door and shoot out, screaming and waving like my deodorant is on fire. Larva bawls a prayer to St. Jude and then she cannonballs out her side.

The truck drives off without us.

We come to our senses then, and we run along behind it for a couple blocks, with me yelling at Larva that she is a idiot and almost got us killed and her yelling the same thing at me. Then, thank God, the truck hits a old wrought-iron fence, and stops. The fence don't look no worse than it did before, but Lout's left headlight is smashed. And I know I got to get them garage men to fix it before Lout sees it or I won't live to see no more parades.

I go straight to the garage. I say, "The headlight is broke." They smirk. Right at that exact minute I feel this tickle. A crawly feeling, sort of. Under my shirt. On my skin. THE MICE.

I am screaming and doing the shimmy at 50 mph around a stack of used tires when finally Larva grabs me and screeches that the mice are gone—running for their lives, probably.

I just stand there for a minute, to pat myself on the

chest and catch my breath. Then I notice THREE garage men have rushed to the truck and they are fixing that headlight as fast as they can.

The things you got to do to get results.

Exposing His Christmas Spirit (or A Holiday Moon)

~~~~~~~~

In the old days, if you saw a decoration on the door, either it was Christmas or somebody was dead. That's what my mother-in-law, Miss Larda, says. But now, if you want to be in style, you got to put stuff up all year long: straw hats at Easter, beads and king cake babies at Carnival, old corn cobs at Thanksgiving, and God knows what else. She says she read that they now got a National Personal Hygiene Week in July and she got no idea what people will put up then but she, for one, is staying home.

My husband Lout claims people put this cheery stuff on their doors to hide the peepholes they look at you through to make sure you ain't no axe-murderer when you come by to borrow a onion or something. He says it shows they got them retentive type-A personalities you hear about.

Well, Lout sure ain't one of them. Not only does he have "I'm a Saints Fan and a Bud Man" bumper stickers all over his truck but he also has two in the bathroom covering up where the tile fell down. And at Christmas, when the rest of our block is lit up like Disney World, we are over here in our Black Hole of Calcutta with a anorexic tree which my kids decorate by standing across the room and throwing clumps of tinsel at it.

But last year was was different. I got to explain this. I don't know about all men, but my husband Lout goes through phases just like my little daughter Gladiola. She had her pacifier phase and her eat-disgusting-things phase and her drop-shoes-in-the-toilet phase. He had his duck-hunting phase and his racetrack phase and his watch-weird-sports-on-TV-and-drink-beer phase. I am waiting for a paint-the-house phase or even a clean-the-attic phase. But this Christmas he hits a hoity-toity phase. And he does a 180-degree about-face and enters our house in a house-decorating contest. (I myself think it is because first prize is the services of a landscape architect for three months. Lout thinks this means he will cut our grass free all summer.) He gets his brothers Leech and Lurch, and they are going to turn my house into a showpiece. Naturally they wait until the day of the judging to start. And then they get into one of them artistic snits.

Lout says we got to decorate tastefully with them teeny white twinkle lights, which he got on sale. But Leech and Lurch got a case of colored bulbs and they say a house done in just white ain't no better than a black-and-white TV. So half my yard gets lit in white and half in color. Lout is a little bit taller and he can throw higher, so stuff like the tops of the crepe myrtle tree and the ligustrum wind up with white lights hanging in them, and their bottom branches and the azaleas and the garbage can are twinkling with colored lights.

Then Lout says to add some real class to this display, we should do what they do Uptown: put a row of paper bags with sand and lighted candles in them on either side of the front walk. Lurch has a dozen of them little paper bags that you get when you buy a pint of gin, and the kids bring sand from their sandpile and I put in the candles I was saving for a hurricane.

But for the centerpiece of the whole display, they are going to have Santa Claus himself, up on the roof looking down the chimney with just his legs and rear end showing. "For a touch of comic amusement," Lout tells me.

By now it is almost dark, so instead of trying to rig a Santa Claus dummy way up there, Lout decides he will just pretend he is a dummy. He puts on some red sweat pants and rubber boots and climbs up to wait for the judges. Meanwhile, Leech hauls out this spotlight he borrowed from somebody's grand opening, and aims it up at the chimney and runs the cord into the kitchen window. Then he lays out the battle plan. When the judges come, Leech will plug in the twinkle lights at the front porch socket; the kids will rush inside and plug in the spotlight in the kitchen, Lurch will run up the walk lighting the candles in the bags, and Lout will stick his head in the chimney and hold still.

When the judges come mincing along, everybody flies into action. The spotlight goes on, but the twinkle lights don't, and I realize all them white and colored strings must have blown that fuse. There's still a lot of light though. All the paper bags are on fire. I guess Lurch must have rushed too fast when he lit them, and maybe there was still a little bit of gin in them bags. What we got here is two rows of little bitty funeral pyres.

But the judges ain't looking at that. Their eyes are following the beam of the spotlight up to the chimney. I look up too.

Lout is lit up like a full moon—or half of one anyway, because that is how far them sweat pants have slipped down.

Well, my friend Awlette won with her front window, which was truly gorgeous—the Madonna and Child done entirely in Rice Krispies. Lout, poor heart, still don't realize what happened and he says this just goes to show some people don't know nothing about taste. But I tell him not to worry, because he made a display that them judges will never forget.

The Humiliation of Household Hints

You know that household hints column they got in the papers with all kinds of real necessary stuff to know like "I used to have a terrible time getting stamps to stay on my envelopes but I have solved the problem. Before I place the stamp on the envelope, I moisten it with my tongue."

Don't them things make you wonder? You feel like a genius because you been knowing about licking stamps for years.

What you want to read is something new. Like "After I have told the bill collector the check is in the mail, I just dash right out to the driveway and roll over the envelope with my car a few times, so it will look like it got caught in some machine at the post office." I would mail that hint in myself except maybe the wrong people might get hold of it.

They also like to print hints where the solution turns out to be worse than the problem. Like "I am so humiliated. There is a streak of mildew on my shower curtain. Please, please help."

A STREAK of mildew? Somebody should book this woman on a tour of Better Bathrooms in New Orleans. She needs the shock therapy.

I myself always told the kids our shower curtain was educational because it was a chance to observe primitive life forms. But now I am feeling guilty because I never felt humiliated. This is one of them mind traps that women get theirselves into all the time. A man, if he even bothered to look at that hint, which he wouldn't unless he was in the bathroom with absolutely nothing else to read but the brand name on the sink, would say to himself, "Dumb woman. I wonder if she got big gazzooms." That's how men think.

But I figure I got to do something about this shower curtain. The solution in the column is "Just take down that nasty curtain. Toss it into the washing machine with a cup of bleach and let it rub-a-dub-dub. In no time it will be clean as a whistle." Well, I can't exactly TOSS it but I cram it in. When I take it out after it's finished rub-a-dubbing, I can't tell if it is clean as a whistle because it has turned into this huge wet wad. It looks like the world's biggest spitball.

So for now we are using black plastic trash bags held together with duct tape. You sure can't find no mildew on them. Of course, they block out the light so you can't see what you're washing, but I figure we all know where to find our armpits anyway.

By now you would think I would give up on them hints. But no, I just got to find something else in there to feel guilty about. And sure enough. Here is a letter from somebody who don't know how to clean out the inside of her coffee maker. Now, I always say, if you can't get to it, God don't intend you to clean it out. But this woman don't see things that way. She is probably the type who takes laxatives. Anyway, the helpful hint is to run it through a cycle with vinegar.

I make the mistake of reading this out loud to my teenage daughter Gumdrop, who is wandering around looking for her shoes. She immediately announces that all her friends' mothers clean out their coffee makers, and she hopes nobody finds out her mother don't.

I got to explain. Gumdrop is at the sensitive age. This means she believes that everybody in her family is a closet lunatic and the second she lets her guard down, we will humiliate her in front of her friends, the only normal people in the world.

I think, why start up with her over a coffee maker? So I pour vinegar in the thing and turn it on, and I get back hot vinegar, which I put in a jelly glass to cool off.

Gumdrop is still hanging around, and I realize this was just a preliminary bout. What she really wants to talk about is how all her friends' mothers are buying their daughters teeny miniskirts like I won't buy for Gumdrop because they are so short, they should come with matching chastity belts.

I am trying to say this in a nice way, and I don't

hardly notice when my husband Lout walks in for a glass of water. But instead, he picks up the vinegar and puts some ice cubes in it. I still don't notice. Then all of a sudden he says, "Gumdrop, you better put them shoes on, Sweetheart. I think you got a little problem." Gumdrop just stares at him like he has turned into a lizard in front of her eyes. So he goes off and plops down in front the TV, rattling his ice cubes. Then he yells "WHOOH! I can still smell it in here. Gumdrop, you scrub them feet!"

Well, Gumdrop has locked herself in her room and is crying her heart out before I realize that Lout ain't smelling anybody's feet. He is holding a glass of vinegar under his nose.

It takes me half the night to get Gumdrop calmed down. And Lout goes off to spend his evening watching the Wednesday night all-girl oil wrestling at the Sloth Lounge, where he says he can find peace and quiet and something decent to drink.

Next time, I will just read the comics. They are closer to real life anyway.

Egyptian Hat and Jabba the Cat

N ow, just because I got a cat lying around the house, don't mean I am what you would call a cat fancier. You ain't going to catch me running to Schwegmann's to buy him liver cookies shaped like mice, or knitting a kitty sweater, or bringing home one of them books that are supposed to tell you what your cat is thinking.

I know what that cat is thinking. He is thinking it is high time somebody improved the service around here.

Cats are like that. It don't matter if you give them a roof over their head and free meals. They reserve their right to be picky. A cat will sit there and watch you eat a oyster loaf until you actually feel guilty enough to toss him a fried oyster. Then he will sniff it and decide he don't care for the seasoning and leave it on the floor.

Cats also reserve their right to lounge wherever they choose. (We can say they lie around, but cats lounge. I know that without reading that book, too.) It don't matter if you are already occupying the chair they happen to choose. They will just lounge on you. Or on the movie section of the paper, or the road map, or anything you got spread out on the floor that you want to look at. I guess they figure, if you want to look at something, you can look at a cat.

Our cat, who we call Minny even though he don't answer to it—he would probably rather be called "Sir"—is like all cats. Only fatter. A lot fatter.

When I lost my better judgment and took Minny in on a cold and stormy night a couple of years back, he was this skinny little kitten with ribs you could count. Today, after two years as a Gunch, he looks like a cat version of Jabba the Hutt. I don't think he even HAS ribs no more. He probably digested them.

Not that he worries none about his figure. I guess he figures as long as his fur don't feel tight, why should he care?

And besides, he has turned into a conversation piece. People who come to the door wanting to discuss whether we are Saved or want aluminum siding or something take one look at this cat, lose track of what they was saying, and blurt out stuff like "What you feed that thing? Suckling pigs?" And I always take up for him, God knows why. I tell them, "He got glands, poor thing." Or "He got big bones."

I learned them lies from my sister-in-law, Larva, who is on the chunky side. Larva says she always knows when it's time to go on a diet, because the bathtub don't fit no more and she got to wash one leg a time. But Larva is fun to be around, and that goes a long way. You can't say that about somebody which you have to prod with your toe every couple of hours to tell if he's dead or not. That's how it is with this cat.

Of course, every now and then he lounges himself into trouble. Like the time I threw some of my delicate unmentionables in the drier on "fluff," not having no idea he has chose to lounge in there for his after-breakfast nap. Immediately I hear this THUMP, THUMP, THUMP and I think the drier is broke and yank it open. Well, out he shoots with every hair on his body standing on end, either from static electricity or from indignation, or both, looking twice as big as his normal self, like some monster lint ball come alive. Anybody would've screamed and got hysterical. When my husband Lout comes running, I still ain't ready to get down off the washing machine, but the cat is lounging on the couch, licking his fur back in place.

That was only a minor adventure. He had a big one last week, when my daughter Gumdrop is finishing up her social studies project on King Tut for the school fair. King Tut is the Egyptian pharaoh that passed on and got buried with a huge solid gold mask on. Gumdrop has been working for weeks making a life-size drawing of this mask, and she is going to make it look like gold by coating it with glue and sprinkling glitter all over it.

Anyway, she gets it all drawn and she lays it on the kitchen floor, and she slathers on glue and glitter, and she turns around for a minute, and Minny chooses that minute to lounge on it. She yells at him to shoo, and he don't shoo. He just keeps lounging, but he starts to look panicky.

Gumdrop has used one of them super strong glues that they say can hold an elephant. I don't know about that, but it sure works on a fat cat. The only thing to do is fill up the sink with warm water, and drop Tut and Minny in, and hope they separate. When Minny hears the water running, he gathers up all the strength in his big body, and arches up and tears himself off Tut and leaps for the curtains, where he thinks he will be safe. He sticks to the curtains.

Gumdrop fixes Tut by covering up the cat stomach print with glue and glitter. Tut winds up with hollowed-out cheeks but you'd expect that in a dead person. I wind up with furry curtains and Minny winds up with a bald spot where the vet had to shave him.

So don't mistake me for no cat fancier, even if we do have a cat lounging around the house in a sweater.

Never Dress Like a Portable Toilet

If you remember just one thing in your life, remember this. NEVER DRESS LIKE A PORTABLE TOI-LET. Write it down. This might be the most important advice you ever got.

Not that I am saying you were going to do that anyway. But you never know what is going to happen.

See, my husband Lout and myself and his family, we all dress up alike on Mardi Gras. Because people on floats throw more trinkets and doubloons and beads to ten or twelve people dressed up alike than to one person dressed the very same way. One time we were all trash cans, and we came home with bags full of long beads and cups and bikini panties and all kinds of stuff. But my brother-in-law Lurch, he got separated from the rest of us, and spent the day leaning on a lamp post and all he got was three chicken bones and a empty beer can.

Anyway, remember how a couple years ago Mardi Gras came during that miserable war in the middle of the East? The Gunch family decided they just had to do something to salute the troops. And my husband Lout's youngest sister, Gloriosa, comes up with one of her brilliant ideas. She guarantees it will get us on TV.

We will be oak trees with yellow ribbons around us. We can wear tree branches on our heads, which will be perfect for catching beads, she says. You look up in a tree after a parade and they got all kinds of beads. Trees catch more beads than anybody.

Well, that convinces us.

Except for Lout. Lout wants to be macho and dress up like one of them patriotic missiles.

Now when we was trash cans, we just wore signs on the front of us that said "Throw Trash Here" and hats with flaps on them that said "PUSH." But this year everybody wants to go whole hog. Gloriosa says we can make cylinders out of poster paper and color them like tree bark and wear them around us like naked people wear barrels. I says it is going to take a lot of poster paper to go around some of us, but I ain't going to argue with any costume I don't have to sit down and sew sequins on. So Gloriosa rushes off to some discount paper place and comes back with her car full of poster paper and everybody comes to my house and I set out a few King cakes for snacks and we all get busy turning ourselves into trees.

Except Lout. He is determined to be a missile, so he paints his cylinder white and blue. But he forgets one thing. Missiles are very tall and skinny, and Lout is short and wide. He would make a good cannonball, but we got the wrong war for that. When he finishes and tries it on, we all think one thing and finally my little nephew Locust says right out loud, just like that kid in the story that blurted out the emperor didn't have no clothes on.

"Uncle Lout," he says. "You look like a portable terlit."

It's the truth. Lout stares in the mirror awhile, and then he decides to make the best of it, and he draws a door on the front and he puts a crescent moon instead of stars on the side.

And the next day the whole grove of us, plus Lout, are strutting up St. Charles Avenue. When we go past where Channel 8 has their cameras set up, Gloriosa sucks in her stomach and sticks out her chest so far she rips her bark and we got to patch her up with Scotch tape.

But the real disaster is this. We realize it too late. Tall trees are the ones that catch stuff. Short trees don't catch nothing. And we are short, for trees.

Plus, in a tree suit, you can't bend over. So you can't hit the ground when you hear doubloons tinkle on the sidewalk, and even if you step on one, you can't reach down to pick it up. When you try to catch with your hands, your branches get in the way. The only thing you can do is hold your bag open and hope somebody aims right for it. And that don't happen much.

And you can't sit down on the curb to eat your fried chicken or rest your feet or nothing. And you got to completely strip off your bark just to go to the bathroom.

Speaking of bathrooms, Lout is not doing too good either. He is being pestered by drunks who knock on his door and say they need to use him, and people singing "Heeere's Johnny!" and stuff like that.

But thank God, this truck float named "What a Dog!" rolls up and everybody on it is dressed like different kinds of dogs. They look at us and yell "Trees!" and play like they are having the same reaction to us that the drunks are having to Lout. Then, they throw us practically everything on the truck, and we actually snag some beads on our branches.

Lout still ain't caught nothing, and he goes to find a real bathroom. When he comes out he got about six inches of toilet paper dragging from one foot. He don't notice it and he don't notice the TV cameras either. And he winds up getting on the six and the ten o'clock news instead of Gloriosa. I heard later on the cameraman got a award for that shot, which ran with the "Baby Elephant Walk" in the background.

Lout says from now on he will just wear a bag over his head.

Ninety-Nine Percent Perspiration

~~~~~~~~~~

I always thought that when somebody invented something, they did it to make life easier. Like for instance, they invented living room couches so we don't all have to squat on rocks when we watch TV. And frost-free freezers, so we don't have to thaw them out every six months with a hair drier. That kind of stuff.

Well, I hate to say this, but lately they have run out of ideas. So they started inventing stuff to make life harder.

Now you can buy a coffee-bean grinder, so when you stagger into the kitchen every morning, instead of scooping some factory-ground coffee out the bag, you throw the beans in your grinder and switch it on. It instantly goes RAT-A-TAT-TAT like a machine gun and you and everybody else in your house wakes right up and hits the floor. After that you don't even need to drink no coffee.

And they come out with a bread-making machine.

With this, instead of buying a sixty-nine-cent loaf of bread, you buy flour and yeast and oil and whatever else you put in bread, and you measure it all into this machine, and then you get out your mayonnaise and your slice of baloney and wait for the rest of your sandwich to be ready in about a hour. My husband Lout gets it in his head that this would be a nice thing to have because he just loves the smell of warm bread. I tell him he can stick a hamburger bun in his armpit.

And I will never forget that appliance to scramble eggs still in their shells. No more whomping the egg on the edge of the frying pan and stirring it with a fork. No, you carefully punch a tiny hole in the egg, and insert this invention, and turn it on and it whirs around in there and scrambles that egg. Then you remove the invention and maybe paste a label that says "prescrambled" over the hole, and put the egg away. And anybody who checks your egg carton will know you own a egg scrambler.

I think the geniuses they keep in them think tanks up North that come up with these ideas need to try a little harder. Maybe they need to change the water in them tanks.

I can tell them what we need.

Floors that are wired so that when somebody drops their clothes or their books or their toys, a buzzer goes off and if that person don't pick it up in ten seconds they get a electric shock.

Telephones for teenagers that tell them their fifteen minutes is up and to go do their homework and then disconnects them.

Televisions that, when somebody's husband changes the channel more than ten times in ten minutes, will announce, in a voice like Moses, that this husband should do something like fix the sink. Then it will shut itself off with a puff of smoke. Alarm clocks that don't ring or play nice music. They squeal and shout threats, and automatically back up when you reach over to slam them off.

I am thinking about all this on my day off while I am sitting in front of a leaf-and-lawn bag full of unmatched socks. And I happen to look over at my husband Lout's bowling shoes with them nice Velcro fasteners.

A light bulb goes on over my head, and I know I am a genius and I can quit work and the world will beat a path to my door. Because I thought of a invention I know how to make.

It is so brilliant. Everybody knows that a washing machine will eat half of every pair of socks, unless you go find a safety pin and pin them together when you take them off, which of course you never do. But if you got a strip of Velcro around the cuff, you can just touch them together and throw them in the wash and they will come back out together. So that same day I run to Krauss's Department Store and I buy Velcro and new socks for Lout and the kids and I sit down in front of "Oprah" and sew strips all around them sock cuffs.

Next morning, everybody goes off wearing new socks.

And they all come home wearing no socks.

I tell them there are always a few bugs to work out in a new invention.

Like, if you got on a skirt, like my daughter Gumdrop, and socks with Velcro cuffs, and your teacher makes you stand with your feet together, after that you have to walk with very small steps.

And if you cross your legs at the ankle and you jump up in a hurry, maybe you will fall flat on your face.

And if you are wearing polyester knit pants, like Lout, and you cross your ankle over your knee, when you get up you might hop around awhile with your ankle still up, and the other people at work might laugh at you a little, and maybe lay down and pound the floor. Especially if you forget and do it two or three times.

I tell them that with new inventions, you got to have patience. But they don't have no patience, and they all threaten to leave home forever and stuff. So I give up, and get out the toenail scissors and take off the strips.

Next week I will spend my day off prescrambling eggs.

Nerves of Steel;
Nothing to Live For

~~~~~~~~~~~

N ot to get sentimental or nothing, but if you are a mother, you know your baby is always going to be your baby no matter how old he gets. You look at his face, and you still see them little soft cheeks you wiped Popsicle drool off of. You look at his size-twelve shoes, and you see the tiny little feet that toddled in the kitty litter. You look at his big hairy knees, and you see the same fat baby legs that peddled his tricycle around the block while he was stark naked.

So it is perfectly normal to be terrified out of your mind to ride in a car he is driving.

Which explains a lot. I always noticed that my mother-in-law flinched and clutched her bosom whenever my husband Lout drove her someplace, but I just thought she was old and had nerves. Now I know better.

See, my little daughter Gumdrop has just made fifteen, which is just thirteen years out of diapers as far as I am concerned, but the State of Louisiana says that makes her old enough to drive a car.

So she wants to take this drivers' ed class they got at school that will cost us about the same amount we paid to the doctor when she was born.

Lout says it is ridiculous to pay to teach her something he knows himself, so he leads the way out to the car and and he lets her slide in behind the wheel. He opens the passenger door and motions for me to get in. Then he runs and stands on the porch and yells, "DRIVE AWAY FROM THE HOUSE!" and starts making hand signals like he is talking to the deaf. I see I am going to be the one to teach her to drive.

The thing about teaching somebody to drive is that you can't remember how you do it yourself. She says, "Do I step on the gas when I turn the key?" and I got to hold a imaginary wheel in my hands and turn a imaginary key and watch to see if my foot goes up and down or not.

But that don't matter because it takes me just over a minute to forget how to speak English entirely. At first I am fine. We are half a block away from the corner, and I decide to remind her about the stop sign that is coming up. I say, pretending to be cheerful, "Stop at the stop sign." She screeches, "WHERE?" and slams on the brake and we come to a dead halt in the middle of the block. I say, "STOP SIGN THERE!" and point and do little rocking movements to make the car go. So she stomps down on the gas and in half a second we are at the corner and there is a truck coming. I pound my foot on the spot on the floor where the brake pedal would be

if I was driving and I screech, "HERE! TRUCK! STOP!,"
which makes no sense unless I am calling a dog named
"Truck Stop." But Gumdrop stops anyway, thank God,
and we are saved.

I drive us home and tell Lout to take out a loan and
pay for that driver's ed course. Let somebody else be
carted off to the psychiatric ward.

So she takes the course and in six weeks she comes
home with a little certificate that says she can drive.

That don't really mean she can drive. She still has
to get her driver's license. And in Louisiana, you can't
get your driver's license until you come up with a birth
certificate. Not the cute little birth certificate with tiny
footprints on it you been saving in a shoe box for fifteen
years. A certified certificate that you got to get by
standing in line at City Hall for a hour and paying eight
dollars.

After that you go to the Driver's License Bureau
and get in another line. A line that is probably longer
than any ladies' room line in the civilized world. (Almost as long as the one in the Louisiana Superdome,
which lasts from week to week and makes some ladies
permanent Dome residents during football season.)
Once you have got to the front of this line, either they
tell you it looks like rain and they ain't going to test
anybody else today, or else they give up and actually
give you the test.

Now, you would think people who give driving tests
for a living would have nerves of iron. It should be a

requirement for the job. They should say it right in the classified ad. "Wanted. Nerves of iron. Nothing to live for. Good pay. Apply City Hall."

But evidently they just got normal people like you and me. This is why you got to wait in line so long. Them testers are getting up their courage. They probably spend hours in the back room, arguing about whose turn it is to go next.

"I got four kids. You go." "Me? I'm young. I got my whole life ahead of me." "Ha."

Anyway this pale little man gets in the car with Gumdrop, lurches around the block with her, and jumps out and tells her she passed. I personally think he would have told Koko the gorilla she passed if it meant he could get out the car.

But she is grinning from ear to ear and she tells me to hop in and she will drive us home. Of course I got to get in. But I clutch my bosom. And I moan and I flinch. I am getting old, and I got nerves.

Ode du Toilette

~~~~~~~~~

I ain't no pervert or nothing, but I know a lot about
restrooms. I got a bladder the size of a Rice Krispie
and I also got kids. It is a mathematical fact that KID
(is to) STRANGE BATHROOM as DOG (is to) FIRE
HYDRANT. They should teach you that in algebra class.

And naturally, you got to go in there to supervise or
risk the consequences. (See Chapter 2, "Who's the
Boss?")

So I am waiting for my little daughter Gladiola to
come out the restroom stall, trying to be patient and not
breathe too deep, and I start thinking about how I could
write a book on restrooms. All kinds of them; from the
ones that got everything you could dream of, and are
worth a special trip; down to the kind that smells like
the elephant house at the zoo.

It would give me something to do while I am standing outside of a stall listening to Gladiola sing to herself
and trying not to look at the ladies behind me who are
shifting from foot to foot.

Ode du Toilette

Normal sinks would get a high recommendation. Not the kind with handles you got to keep holding to keep the water running, so you wash one hand, and then you wash the other hand, and then you wash the first hand again because God knows what's been on that handle, and you can keep that up all night.

And not the kind that don't turn off at all, and there you are twisting the handle and thinking you broke the pipe and then it snaps itself off, real smug, because it is operated by a tiny automatic timer.

Now in the stall itself, I would recommend toilets that could be comfortably flushed with your foot. Not the kind that have a ghost flusher, so as soon as you stand up, it flushes, which makes you jump and stare around thinking there is somebody in there with you. Come to find out, this toilet operates by electric eye. What I want to know is exactly where IS this eye? And just WHAT does it see?

Anyway, I myself was brought up to be a foot flusher. And I have noticed that toilet engineers, who must have been raised by mothers who went right ahead and let them flush that flusher with their hands, are little by little raising the flushers higher and higher. I think it is a plot against foot flushing. If you are in high heels you really got to rare back to get your foot up there. One time I lost my balance and keeled over backward right out the stall and landed on my mother-in-law, thank God, who cushioned my fall.

Somebody needs to inform them engineers, in a delicate way, that we got a problem here.

They could also talk to the toilet paper roll engineers. It used to be that you checked the stall, saw that it had a nice little roll of toilet paper, said, "Thank God," and went in. But lately, you look in and what do you see? A toilet paper roll the size of a tractor tire. I wonder about them things. Why does anybody want a giant roll of toilet paper? Do the industrial toilet paper companies have a irresistible slogan? "Enough to wipe ten thousand hinies"? Or "If Andre the Giant used YOUR restroom, he'd want THIS roll of toilet paper"?

But you know what happens when you try to get one of them huge rolls to actually dispense toilet paper. You tug on the end of the paper and it don't roll. You get a whole square if you're doing good. Andre the Giant would be in that stall three months. Is that what they want?

So then they come up with the super-efficient triple toilet paper roll dispenser, the kind that has three rolls. After the first one is used, the second one is supposed to automatically fall into place. Only generally the second one falls prematurely, and blocks roll number one so it don't want to turn, and there you are, back to getting it one square at a time again. That's where the expression "Back to Square One" came from.

And of course there are air driers. They have them to dry your hands, so they don't have to give you towels. It won't be long before one of them engineers decides it will save money to have air driers in stalls, so they don't have even to give you paper. My mother-in-law thought of this and so she always carries a little packet of Kleenex tissues in her purse.

I'll bet most toilet paper roll engineers are men. They don't even have to stand in line. Usually they all just stand next to each other at that trough or whatever it is they use. What I want to know is, how can they zip up, walk out the bathroom, and start harrumphing and acting dignified with each other after that?

And over at the ladies' room, we are still standing in line.

What we really need is a digital timer on the inside of each stall that gives you statistics. It would read, for instance, "You have occupied this stall for (3) minutes and (27) seconds. There are now (9) ladies and (2) squirming children waiting in line."

Then I just have to teach Gladiola to read.

The Mother-in-Law
of Invention

~~~~~~

My husband Lout, his idea of summer fun is holding one armpit at a time up to the air conditioner vent. Not that I blame him—New Orleans ain't no breezy outdoor paradise in August.

There is no way you can leave the house and still be cool unless you go stark raving naked. What you do, of course, is wear shorts, like me, or a big flowered muumuu, like my mother-in-law Miss Larda, and even then you got problems. You get in a car which is hot enough to cook lasagna in, and try to sit down without letting the backs of your legs touch the seat, and you drive off holding the steering wheel with the ends of your fingernails.

Of course if your car has air conditioning, you just hang in there for a few minutes until it cools down and then you can ride along and listen to nice music on the radio and look smug.

But if you are like some of us who got to depend on

Mother Nature to keep us comfortable, you got a choice.

You can open your windows and let the fresh air blow in, which will both cool you off and give you a hair style to match your feather duster. Or you can keep them windows rolled up tight and develop a aroma that reminds people that they got to clean their turtle bowl.

I decide there has to be a better way. So I go out and I pay $4.99 for this little plastic personal fan with batteries and a suction cup which you lick and and stick on the dashboard. I discover that this will churn up a little breeze, until the suction cup gets tired of sucking on the dashboard and makes a leap and flips into your crotch. Which might make you temporarily drive strangely enough to attract a policeman's attention. Now maybe you would explain to him that you was driving with a electric fan in your crotch, but me, I would rather just pay the ticket.

So I am telling Lout about this and he is sitting there, like he does, staring in his beer. After a while he says, "You know, Modine, there is lots of air OUTSIDE a car." This is the kind of deathless observation he usually comes up with after a few beers, so I don't say nothing.

Then he goes on. "Why move around the hot air inside the car? What you need to do is funnel just the right amount of outside air INSIDE." Now, in August, Lout usually moves pretty slow, like a slug. But he is excited now. He strides over to the vacuum cleaner and he yanks off the floor attachment, which got a wide part that leads into a neck that leads into the hose, and he says, perfectly serious, "This could make us rich, Modine," and he marches outside with it.

After a while he comes back and says he needs me, as a objective second party, to test-drive his invention. He has the car front window rolled down, but just a little, enough so that there is space in front of it, and in that space he has wedged my vacuum cleaner attachment, with the wide part outside and the hose part inside the car. This is his invention.

"Get up to about thirty miles an hour, Modine, and then just pick up your end of the hose and aim it at your face, or your neck, or under your arm or anywhere else you want to get cool, heh, heh," and he wiggles his eyebrows up and down. I ignore that. I check to make sure he has cleaned the dirt out of this hose, and I drive away from him.

And believe it or not, the invention works. I hold the hose to my face and cool air rushes in and it actually feels good. Until all of a sudden the outside part falls off, and I got to make a U-turn and leap out the car and get honked at while I scrabble in the street to rescue my vacuum cleaner.

Lout says this is just one of them temporary setbacks like scientists have all the time. In a couple hours he is ready for a objective second party to test-drive his revised design, but this time he knows better than to ask me. He calls up Miss Larda.

The revised version is a bleach bottle with the bottom cut off tied to the outside rearview mirror, with my vacuum cleaner hose taped on and trailing inside the window like before.

Miss Larda gets in and says she ain't taking no chances, so she puts both hands on the wheel and clamps the hose under one thigh and twists the end up so it is aiming at her face, and off she goes. At first, it works fine. But then, she must shift in her seat. Anyway, the hose gets caught under the hem of her muumuu, which starts filling up like a balloon. That actually feels good for a while, until she notices people in other cars are looking at her funny. So she right away pulls off to the side to get herself decent, and it ain't her fault about them cars that ran off the road. Of course, when the cop shows up, there is no way she is going to tell him she was riding around with a vacuum cleaner hose up her dress. "What kind of pervert would he think I am, Modine?" she says to me later. "He would probably arrest me for that." And she don't argue about the ticket.

So the New Orleans Traffic Court made plenty of money off us this month. They probably bought a air conditioner.

Sizable Fashion
Problems

~~~~~~~

I just wish I had the figure of a clothes hanger.

I am thinking this while I thrash through the dress racks at the mall, desperate like usual, since everything I got in my closet has either been washed with red socks or has something like "Check Your Fly" written across the front of it.

And I can't help noticing how cute them hangers look in their little outfits. Some of them are dangling on their own display hooks around the store, wearing these adorable dresses with coordinating blazers, and wide belts wrapped two or three times around the waistline, and scars at their skinny little necks that just perfectly set off the dress colors.

Of course, people like you and me who actually pay good money for these outfits don't look near as good in them as hangers do. This is because we got body parts like stomachs and buns and bosoms sticking out all over, which interfere with the design of the clothes and probably makes fashion designers very annoyed. It must be like Michelangelo trying to paint a gorgeous picture on lumps of Jell-O.

Naturally, designers got ways to get even. We think it is a accident that when we put on a dressy dress with a dropped waistline tastefully accented by a single sequined rose, the single sequined rose always winds up tastefully accenting our crotch. Or when we pull on one of them jeweled sweaters, and two of them jewels perch right where pasties would go. Hah. That ain't no accident. That is what you call creative revenge.

But it ain't nothing compared to how creative them designers get when they sew in the size label. Now once in a while they just stick it on the neckline or the waistline where you expect it. But that is just to tease you. They really get their kicks by sticking it halfway down the leg, or under the zipper, or in the armpit—so you got to turn a outfit inside out and upside down before you know if it is anywhere near your size.

Or maybe you don't find no label at all, but you try it on anyway and it fits perfect so you buy it and nobody tells you until three months later you been going around with a little flag waving from your behind that reads "X-LARGE WIDE." This actually happened to my sister-in-law Larva.

Now my shopping troubles ain't nothing compared to poor Larva's, because she wears them hard-to-find largish sizes. Anyway, in August, "Angela" (the New Orleans version of "Oprah") did a show on Elvismaniacs, which Larva is. And Larva gets a last-minute invite to be in the live audience. Well, it was a crisis.

Larva has half a day to find something decent to wear. "I can't do it, Modine," she says to me. "Not only do I got to find a bunch of things that might be the right size, but then I got to grab a sales clerk who will tap in the secret code for the fitting room and give me a little plastic number that says the maximum number of garments I can carry in; then I got to squeeze into them garments; then I got to look in the mirror; promise God to go on a diet; rush out; get more garments; track down the salesclerk again, get her to tap in the secret code again . . ."

Well, nobody in our family has ever been on TV before, unless you count the time my husband Lout dressed like a portable toilet on Mardi Gras, or my brothers-in-law Lurch and Leech jumping around and making faces over the announcer's shoulder after a Saints game. So we ain't about to let this chance slip by. My mother-in-law Miss Larda, and my other sister-in-law, Gloriosa, and my daughter Gumdrop and myself, we all march with Larva right into the Fat Lady Department at J. C. Penney's. Each of us grabs the maximum number of garments allowed, all in Larva's size, and we rush into a fitting room. Then we realize we look like a bunch of perverts, and we rush out again and go into adjacent fitting rooms. And we pitch the dresses to her over the top of the partition.

At first it seems like even this won't work. Them

designers just ain't so creative when it comes to large sizes. All the dresses got bold stripes, or are made out of real shiny fabrics, or are big floral prints. "I see I got a choice," Larva yells to us. "I can look like I am wearing a awning. Or I can look like a kitchen appliance. Or I can dress like my own sofa."

Then Gumdrop gets a idea. She zips off to the Skinny Lady Department and comes back with this straight black dress, which looks fine on Larva if she don't zip up the back. And we get a nice big pink blazer and put it over that, and voilà, she is in pink and black and ready for "Angela." As long as she keeps the blazer on and don't shrug.

We all sit around the TV at my house to watch and we distinctly see the top of her head just before the first commercial and her hands clapping—I know it was hers because she has on my Flamingo Flush nail polish. And afterwards we talk about how good she did, even though she didn't jump around behind Angela and make faces. My brothers-in-law were kind of disappointed about that. But Elvis would have been proud.

The Devil Made Her Do It

~~~~~~

My mother-in-law Miss Larda, she thinks it is a crying shame that kids got to be terrified of Halloween these days.

So she sits my three down and she gives them her little pep talk. "It don't matter whether it's Halloween or not," she says, real philosophical. "If it is your turn to eat a candy bar poisoned with arsenic, you will eat it. If it is your turn to trip over the curb in the dark and fall down a manhole and be washed into the sewer system, you will be washed into the sewer system. God decides these things, not you. So relax. Enjoy life."

Well, up until that inspiring speech, my kids never worried their heads about Halloween at all. To them, it was just another day to get something for nothing, like Mardi Gras and Christmas and Easter.

But now they are sitting there with their eyes bugging out. And Miss Larda winds up by saying that she hopes they understand Halloween is a happy time for lots of fun. As long as they watch out for satanists.

I got to explain. Miss Larda, she believes every word that comes out Geraldo Rivera's mouth. And ever since he did this show about satanists, Miss Larda been seeing satanists behind every azalea bush. According to her, satanists particularly got it in for cats, and some people who have changed one too many litter boxes probably sign up to be satanists just for that reason. She tells my daughter Gumdrop that on Halloween, she better keep a eye on her cat, Minny.

It is hard NOT to keep an eye on Minny. He kind of dominates the room, like a orange fur couch. This ain't no cat your average satanist would want to mix it up with. He looks like a Japanese sumo wrestler with fur. And he don't stand for no foolishness. Don't even think about serving his meals late. You just might become his meal.

But Gumdrop just loves her Minnycat, and so she is very worried. She figures she better hide him away on Halloween night. She takes all her shoes out her clothes closet and arranges Minny's food and water and litter box on the floor. She gets his little round pillow he has liked to sit on since he was a kitten. Then she wedges a electric fan on the top shelf, aiming down, so Minny won't get overheated. Well, Minny thinks he is in cat heaven. Nice and cool and dark and everything he needs within paw's reach. He curls up happy on his pillow, lapping over the sides like he is trying to hatch it. And we don't hear a mew out of him.

Until about four in the morning. The house must

settle a little or something, because that electric fan falls off the closet shelf. It don't hit Minny, but it don't please him neither. It lands on its back and sucks up one of them Odor Eater insoles that Gumdrop has left on the floor and starts flapping that around in its blades.

Now some people say, like they have had long talks with cats about this, that cats are very cool and self-possessed and don't show their emotions. Well, this is because they don't generally have emotions to show. What does a cat have to get excited about, as long as his food bowl stays full? But you shut a cat in a closet with a Odor Eater flapping out a electric fan, and that cat is definitely going to show his emotions. He ain't going to keep no stiff upper lip.

Minny yowls and balls up into a cannonball and hurls himself at the door. Then, just in case he got confused in the dark and that ain't the door, he hurls himself into the other three walls of the closet. Then he starts the whole thing over again.

This jolts my son Gargoyle awake, since his bed is right on the other side of one of them walls. He don't know what is flapping and thumping, but it is coming from his sister's room. He has the automatic brother reaction—get back at her. He grabs his plastic pumpkin full of candy, which he has hid under the bed, and starts whomping the wall with it.

So now we have flappings and thumpings and whompings and Gumdrop wakes up and naturally decides the satanists have come. She has the automatic

teenager reaction—grab the phone. She is going to dial
911 over and over until somebody answers, but since
she is half asleep she hits the buttons wrong and dials
916-something, and wakes up some guy in California
and yells at him that satanists are after her cat.

By this time I myself have woke up. I throw open
the closet and Minny streaks straight under Gumdrop's
bed where he gets stuck because he is too fat to fit.
Gumdrop stops yelling and looks at the phone receiver
in her hand and says, real dignified, "Pardon me," and
slams it down. Then we all together lift the bed and let
Minny out.

So no harm done. Except to our nerves. And that
guy in California. I hope it was Geraldo.